Contents

Preface

Over the last few years concerns have been raised in both the public and professional media, regarding young people and alcohol. One reason for this has been the publicity surrounding the introduction of new ranges of alcoholic drinks, in particular, 'alcopops'. It therefore seems an opportune time to review the research literature currently available on alcohol and young people aged between 11 to 24 years, and to consider the issues it raises in relation to health promotion.

Whereas drinking alcohol is a normal part of life for many adults in the UK, there is a range of harms associated with its consumption. Preventing harm related to alcohol in the young is complex, and needs to take into account the different patterns of drinking adopted at different ages, together with the varying social contexts in which it occurs. In order to minimise the risk of harm to young people from drinking alcohol, we need to think about it in relation to their perceptions, behaviour and attitudes, which are central to this review. It provides a detailed overview for professionals with an interest in young people and alcohol which will enable them to consider how to achieve a balance between educating young people about drinking sensibly, and preventing unnecessary harms, by communicating with them in a language they will relate to and understand.

Moira Kelly
Research manager

ABOUT THE AUTHOR

Linda Wright is currently a freelance health promotion consultant, specialising in drug education and research. With more than twenty years' experience in health promotion work she has worked in a wide range of settings. She managed a health authority health promotion service for ten years and has been a Senior Research Fellow and a Lecturer in health education at the University of Durham. She worked for TACADE for five years before joining the brave new world of freelance work in January 1995.

Her involvement in alcohol issues dates back to 1977, when she was actively involved in the North East Alcohol campaign and co-authored *Drinking choices: a training manual for alcohol educators*. She is a trained voluntary alcohol counsellor and was instrumental in setting up the Cleveland Council on Alcohol. She is currently completing her PhD thesis on alcohol and youth workers. She has extensive experience of developing and delivering training on health promotion and alcohol education and is author of several teaching and training resources. Her recent work on alcohol includes: *More drinking choices* (published by the HEA) and *Carrying the can: working with girls and young women on alcohol issues; Lager and Blastaways: an alcohol training programme for youth workers* and *Six pack: compendium of games for alcohol education* (published by TACADE).

Executive summary

This review of the literature on young people and alcohol was commissioned by the Health Education Authority to support the work of their alcohol programme. The remit was to undertake a literature review that would explore young people's knowledge about alcohol, their attitudes and their drinking behaviour. The age band set for the review was 11- to 24-year-olds, with the main interest in 11- to 20-year-olds.

The review concentrates on research published in English since 1980 and on data and research from the UK. Studies from elsewhere are included, if relevant to young people in the UK.

1. Young people's drinking behaviour

1. Accurate measurement of young people's alcohol consumption is difficult due to the bias inherent in self-reported behaviour, lack of standard questions and measures and young people's consumption of non-standard drinks. Measurement and classification of young people's alcohol consumption is not consistent between studies.

2. Prevalence of young people's alcohol consumption has been measured since the 1970s. Studies commonly involve single-phase, cross-sectional surveys. Continuing monitoring studies have recently been established.

3. Drinking alcohol begins at ages 8–12, with virtually all 12- to 14-year-olds having had some experience of drinking. However, the majority of young teenagers (11–16) do not drink regularly, and most of those who do drink, consume only small amounts.

4. Between the ages of 11 and 16, young people develop from taking the occasional sip of alcohol to being on the verge of drinking like adults; from drinking (mainly) under adult supervision to drinking independently.

5. There are different drinking patterns among schoolchildren in each of the four countries in the United Kingdom and there is considerable regional variation within countries. Direct comparison of data from different studies and countries is limited due to the methodological differences. Schoolchildren's experience of drinking is least in Northern Ireland and greatest in Wales.

6. There is no clear evidence that young people are starting to drink earlier and the proportion of non-drinkers among 11- to 16-year-olds in England and Scotland has remained at about 40% for the last 20 years.

7. Once they start to drink, young teenagers are drinking larger amounts, more frequently.

8. Young teenagers are also increasingly involved in heavy sessional drinking or 'binge drinking'.

9. Young teenage boys drink more alcohol than girls and they drink more frequently, a pattern that continues into adulthood. The frequency of girls' drinking is increasing at a faster rate than that of boys' so that gender differences are diminishing.

10. Between the ages of 16 and 18, young people in England rapidly acquire adult drinking habits, in terms of drinking prevalence, consumption levels and settings for drinking. Mid-teens is the period when young people become experienced drinkers and drinking alcohol becomes the norm for the peer group.

11. There is no marked increase in drinking at 18, when it becomes legal to buy alcohol. Up to 16/17, there is no difference between the proportions of males and females who drink (although big differences in the amounts they drink). After 17 young men are more likely to be drinkers than young women; 16–18 is the peak age for young women's drinking in terms of frequency and quantity of alcohol consumed. For young men, consumption continues to rise and peaks at 18–21.

12. Young adults aged 18–24 are the heaviest drinking group in the population and their drinking is increasing. Four in ten males and one in five females in this age group are drinking above the weekly sensible

drinking levels; 6% of young women drank over 35 units a week in 1996, twice the proportion recorded in 1994. Young women are the only population sector to show an increase in drinking at harmful levels.

13. Among adults, heavy sessional or 'binge' drinking is most prevalent among young adults aged 18–24, especially young men.

14. The majority of under-16s do *not* drink to excess. Consuming alcohol is normal behaviour across the older adolescent age group. Most 16- to 24-year-olds have been drunk and are involved in occasional heavy drinking sessions, although only a minority do so more frequently than once or twice a month.

15. There is little data on socio-economic and educational factors and young people's alcohol consumption. The picture is tentative and confusing, but suggests that 11- to 15-year-olds from better-off families and who have low educational expectations are the group most likely to be frequent drinkers. Finance appears to be an important factor in accounting for variations in alcohol consumption among older teenagers. By their early 20s, it is individuals in the higher socio-economic groups who are more likely to be drinking at risky or unsafe levels

16. Young people alter their drinking habits as their circumstances change or they enter different life stages. Students are more likely to drink above recommended weekly limits than their peers in the general population. Marriage or a stable relationship are important moderating influences on young men's drinking habits, which reduce even further when they become parents.

17. Generally, young people in England, Scotland and Wales are introduced to alcohol by their parents in the home, go on to drinking with friends in other places at around 13–14 years of age and begin to drink alcohol in pubs from the age of about 15 upwards.

18. Most under-18s who buy alcohol appear to be able to purchase it easily. A quarter of 11- to 16-year-olds have bought alcohol from an off-licence. There is no evidence that the extent of 'under-age' drinking in licensed premises has increased or decreased in the past twenty years. 'Under-age' drinking appears to be more prevalent in England than in the

rest of the UK, and in England, both sexes are equally likely to drink in pubs 'under-age'.

19. Pubs, clubs and wine bars are the preferred setting for drinking for the 16–24 age group.

20. Following their introduction to drinking alcohol within the family, adolescents incorporate alcohol into their own social lives with their friends. Drinking plays an important part in young people's leisure pursuits.

21. The majority of children up to the age of 12 prefer soft drinks to alcoholic beverages of any kind.

22. Diversification of the drinks market has targeted the youth sector, with a proliferation of new designer drinks and alcopops, characterised by a relatively high %ABV. These have been incorporated into young people's drinking repertoire. The peak age for drinking alcopops is 13–16.

23. Sex differences in alcoholic beverage preferences are apparent even in novice drinkers aged under 16. Young people's beverage preferences are particularly susceptible to fashion and style influences and the new drinks exploit this.

24. Beverage choice is related to drunkenness. Drinking white cider and flavoured wines (both designer drinks) and vodka is related to drunkenness and binge drinking. Consumption of alcopops is not significantly related to drunkenness.

25. It has not been established whether the new drinks encourage more young people to start to drink, or existing drinkers to drink more, rather than simply influencing the beverage preferences of existing drinkers.

26. Young adults have been observed to consciously use alcohol as a mood altering drug and both seek and expect to get drunk, adopting drinking styles which achieve the best 'buzz', in the same way as users of illegal drugs.

27. Very little research has been done in Britain on ethnic and religious differences in young people's alcohol consumption. Among the 11–16 age group, African Caribbean and South Asian young people in the UK drink less than their white peers.

2. Knowledge: What do young people know about alcohol?

1. Young people know about the harmful effects of alcohol and their knowledge develops as they mature.

2. In common with adults, young people's awareness of units and sensible weekly levels is quite high, but the ability to relate these concepts to their own drinking behaviour is less common.

3. Sensible weekly drinking levels have little relevance to young people's chosen pattern of 'binge' drinking. The focus on daily benchmarks in the current sensible drinking guidelines is more relevant to young people's drinking styles. Compared to other adult age groups, young adults (aged 16–24) are less likely to have heard anything about the changes in the sensible drinking levels but also most likely to be interested in them. Young women are the least likely group to have heard about the changes.

4. Young people consider alcohol to be less harmful than other drugs, including illegal substances, caffeine, tobacco and solvents.

5. Young people from minority ethnic groups are less knowledgeable about alcohol.

6. The research data on young people's knowledge about alcohol is based on information considered by researchers as important for young people to know. We know little about the way young people themselves define, prioritise, organise or interpret information about alcohol, in order to make sense of their social worlds.

3. Attitudes to alcohol

1. From an initially neutral stance, young children develop increasingly negative attitudes to alcohol and to drinkers up to the age of about 10 years. They hold stereotypical beliefs about gender roles and are aware of adult motives for drinking.

2. After the age of 10, attitudes to alcohol become more positive in parallel with increased personal experience of drinking. Young drinkers aged 9–15 perceive the social benefits of drinking. The transition from negative to positive attitudes within the 11–13 age group has received little research attention.

3. Among 11- to 16-year-olds, heavier drinkers are more likely to hold positive attitudes to alcohol and to value the social benefits. They are more likely than others to say that they drink to relax, to socialise, for curiosity, to relieve boredom and because all their friends drink. Heavier drinking boys are also more likely to think it is safe to drive after one or two pints.

4. Schoolchildren who drink alcohol are more likely than non-drinkers to express negative attitudes to school and to teachers.

5. 15- to 16-year-olds consider alcohol to be less harmful than any other drug, including cigarettes and caffeine.

6. As young people enter their mid- to late-teens and become more experienced drinkers, so their attitudes change and develop. Most young people, including light/moderate drinkers say they drink for positive reasons. In contrast with younger teenagers, heavier drinking females are significantly more likely to drink to boost their self-confidence. As with younger teenagers, heavier drinkers of both sexes are more likely to say that they drink alcohol 'to get drunk'.

7. From the age of 16, young people hold similar attitudes to alcohol to those held by the general adult population.

8. There is some evidence that, while alcohol comes relatively low on scales of personal concern, it is of greater concern to young people than to

adults. Young people's concerns are about the possible negative consequences of drinking, rather than with drinking *per se*. Young adults may evaluate binge drinking as life enhancing rather than life threatening.

9. Most young adults describe themselves as moderate or light drinkers and only a small minority worry about their drinking.

10. The expectancies associated with drinking alcohol are: appearing adult, disinhibition, reduces tension, enhances sexuality, enhances social interaction, increases assertiveness and facilitates aggression.

11. Young people, especially heavier drinkers, admit to drinking 'to get drunk' and, compared to adults, are more tolerant of drunkenness. They consciously plan to 'binge' drink on certain occasions and perceive that their friends approve of this practice. Young people do not consider the more serious consequences of binge drinking to be likely outcomes; while they believe they have the skills to control their drinking, they may not apply them in binge drinking situations.

12. We currently have little information about social norms for drunken behaviour among young people. Nor do we know much about the self-control strategies that young people adopt. Further research in this area would be useful.

13. Young people are more vigorously anti-drink driving than adults. However, those young people who hold the least emphatic views are those who claim to have driven while intoxicated. In comparison to older adults, young people aged 16–24 are less likely to be able to judge their personal safe limits for driving and more likely to claim to be able to drive without their ability being affected. More British research is needed into young people's attitudes, assessment of risk and behaviour in relation to riding as a passenger with someone who has been drinking.

14. Young people have positive attitudes to the new alcoholic beverages – designer drinks and alcopops. These drinks are particularly appealing to the mid-teen age group. Young people choose alcoholic beverages that are consistent with their attitudes to drinking and their alcohol expectancies.

15. The 15–24 age group, in common with all other ages, think that pubs should have 'atmosphere', and that good ventilation, alcoholic drinks, comfortable seating, soft drinks and decor are important. Atmosphere and music are particularly important to young people.

16. Young people have rather less interest than older people in stricter controls on alcohol sales, advertising or taxation. They share the strong general public support for unit labelling of cans and bottles of alcoholic beverages and for compulsory training courses for publicans and licensees. They also hold rather less strong views than adults do on moral issues.

17. The ethnic group to which young people belong has been largely ignored in attitude studies. More research is needed into the place and meaning of alcohol among young people from minority ethnic groups.

4. Marketing and advertising alcohol

1. Whether advertising causes people, particularly young people, to start drinking, or to continue or increase their consumption has been hotly debated. There is some evidence to suggest a small but significant positive association between young people's exposure to alcohol advertisements, their consumption levels and positive attitudes to alcohol. Further evidence is needed to establish whether the new alcoholic drinks introduced in the last decade encourage more young people to start to drink, or young drinkers to drink more.

2. The 'advertising response function' model explains the general relationship between alcohol advertising and consumption and supports the view that advertising at local level significantly increases consumption.

3. The new designer drinks and alcopops have been successfully labelled, packaged and marketed to appeal to young people. There is considerable evidence that the new drinks appeal to young people, and appeal more to teenagers than those legally entitled to purchase them.

4. British studies have found that young people like, enjoy and remember alcohol advertisements, particularly those shown on television. However, adolescents, including 10- to 13-year-olds, are capable of sophisticated interpretations of the messages, images and targeting of alcohol advertisements, in the same way as adults.

5. Monitoring of alcohol advertisements in the North West of England concluded that two-thirds of the 21 advertisements viewed broke the Advertising Standards code in some way. Half were judged to be aimed at young people and a third featured someone aged under 25.

6. The Advertising Standards code and the drinks industry's voluntary system of regulation on the packaging and marketing of alcopops seem to have a limited effect.

7. Alcohol education can teach young people to resist persuasive alcohol advertising appeals.

5. The influence of parents and peers

1. Cross-sectional studies, consistently show that young people who drink tend to have friends who drink, while those who do not drink tend to have friends who also do not drink.

2. Interpretations of peer group pressure as an explanation for young people's drinking behaviour can equally be viewed as evidence for peer association: young people choose to associate with others whose drinking habits are like their own.

3. Young people are by no means a homogeneous group and different peer groups have different drinking cultures.

4. Children and young people are vulnerable to the effects of adults drinking, particularly parents. Vulnerability includes the direct toxic effect of alcohol on the foetus during pregnancy and indirect effects mediated through other aspects of family life and the social environment.

5. Children of parents who are problem drinkers experience a wide range of problems most of which are not solely or directly due to alcohol. Problems include emotional and behavioural disorders, and low self-esteem. In adolescence this may be manifested as poor educational performance, anxiety, depression, social isolation or anti-social behaviour.

6. The impact of a parental drink problem is strongest in young children and less certain in adolescents.

7. Protective factors which reduce the negative impact of a parental problem drinker on a child are: a close loving relationship with a parent or someone outside the immediate family, a resilient personality and high achievement in some field, for example school, sport, hobby.

8. Family support and cohesion are associated with positive outcomes for young adults, whether or not there is a drink problem in the family. Family life is an important influence on adolescent drinking.

9. Four family socialisation factors – support, control, models and parental attitudes – are independently and additively related to adolescent drinking behaviour, with young people's perceptions of parental attitudes being the most salient factor. The optimal family life for producing sensible drinking among young people seems to be a family that offers moderate levels of support and control, attitudes that support sensible drinking by young people and a model of sensible parental drinking.

10. Parents and peers may exert different types of influence on young people's alcohol use and the pattern may vary for males and females, according to the results of an Australian study. Replicative studies are required to establish the direction and degree of influence of parents and peers in relation to the drinking behaviour of young people in Britain.

6. Alcohol-related harm: What sort of harm does young people's drinking cause?

1. Young people's drinking is associated with a wide range of risks and harms, although the nature of the relationships is often less well established. The clustering of heavy drinking with other risky behaviour

in young people presents difficulties in disentangling the effects of drinking alcohol from other risk factors.

2. The fact that young people are not fully developed means that they face greater risks in using alcohol. Children and adolescents' metabolism of alcohol and their physiological response to intoxication differs from that of adults. Novice young drinkers will experience greater intoxication (for a given amount of alcohol) than regular drinkers, because they will have acquired little physical tolerance to the drug. Young people who weigh less than adults will also achieve a higher blood-alcohol level. Alcohol's depressant effect can more easily produce a fatally toxic overdose in young people.

3. No alcohol problem is exclusive to young people, but there is a discernible pattern of alcohol-related problems. Intoxication, episodic drunkenness or 'binge drinking' are most likely to lead to problems such as violence, crime and accidents. Cancers, heart disease, liver cirrhosis and other health consequences of chronic heavy drinking are rarely seen in young drinkers. Youthful drinking behaviour is not a good predictor of alcohol-related illness or physical dependence in later life.

4. Compared to other age groups, young adults have the highest risk of alcohol dependence and problem drinking, although numerically, problems related to single episodes of intoxication are much more common.

5. Drinking alcohol is a positive experience for most young people. The commonest immediate negative consequences experienced by young drinkers are the physiological responses to alcohol – hangover, nausea, dizziness or falls. Gender differences have been noted in under-18s – young women are more likely to report emotional experiences or negative social consequences, while young men are more likely to report involvement in criminal activities.

6. Accidents are the most important serious negative consequence of young people's drinking. Alcohol is implicated in 20–30% of all accidents. Alcohol is an important contributory factor in facial injuries, especially injuries to young people aged 15–25. Accidents, particularly on the roads and near water are especially common in the under-25s. Drivers

aged under 20 have more accidents than older drivers do, even at blood-alcohol levels below the legal limit, confirming that inexperience in driving and inexperience in drinking are a particularly risky combination. Male drivers in their twenties are the group most likely to fail a breath test or be involved in drink-driving accidents.

7. While alcohol is associated with a wide range of crimes, it is not necessarily the cause of crime. On balance, recent longitudinal studies have found that young people's drinking and offending share common causes rather than drinking causes crime. Young adults (17–24) are known to be the heaviest drinkers in the population and are also the most likely age group to be involved in crime. The rate of convictions for drunkenness peaks at age 18. There is a tendency for most young people to grow out of both types of behaviour, risky drinking and offending, as they reach their mid-20s.

8. While there is ample evidence to implicate alcohol in violent acts, the relationship most strongly supported by the research evidence is that aggressive behaviour is developed early in life and later leads to heavy drinking, especially for young men. Drinking and aggression also have shared antecedents. Alcohol-related violence may have less to do with alcohol per se than with the social context in which people drink, particularly people with aggressive tendencies.

9. How alcohol affects sexual behaviour and whether alcohol use *causes* sexual risk-taking has yet to be established. In the UK, studies suggest a positive *association* between drinking alcohol before sexual activity and not using contraception. Young people *combine* alcohol and sex, especially prior to their first sexual experience. They are more likely than older people to say that emotions influence their drinking and more likely to drink when experiencing positive emotions especially romance and stimulation. The part played by alcohol in sexual risk-taking is bound up in the social rituals, expectancies and meanings placed on drinking and on sex by groups of young people.

10. There is a significant positive correlation between alcohol use and misuse by young people and their use of tobacco and illicit drugs, although little is known of the interrelationships that exist.

7. Understanding young people's drinking

1. In contrast to the considerable descriptive data on young people's drinking, much less is known about *why* British young people drink, the place and meaning of drinking alcohol in young people's lives, the social contexts for drinking and the value attached to alcohol use.

2. Analytical studies have examined three major groups of factors and how they relate to young people's drinking behaviour, especially heavy or risky drinking and alcohol-related risks and harms. The three groups of factors are demographic variables, intra-personal factors, and inter-personal factors and social/environmental influences. There have also been a lesser number of studies attempting to determine how important different factors are in influencing a particular behaviour or consequence of drinking.

3. British analytical studies of young people's drinking are relatively rare and a large proportion of work is derived from North American studies. Cultural differences between young drinkers in the UK and the USA, particularly North American classifications of young heavy drinkers or young problem drinkers, mean that the results of North American analytical studies must be treated with caution.

4. Four theoretical models predominate in analytical studies of young drinkers. These are:

- problem behaviour theory
- social learning theory
- reasoned action/planned behaviour theory
- social/environmental influences.

5. There is some evidence to support each of these theories. The lack of British analytical studies means that there is insufficient direct evidence to support any one theory in preference to another, or to enable a convincing synthesis of several differing perspectives to be prepared.

6. Interpretations derived from the relatively few qualitative and ethnographic studies support the view that the social contexts for young

people's drinking are an important key to understanding alcohol's place and meaning. As young people's social worlds are diverse and local, care must be taken in extrapolating conclusions from these studies to young people in general.

7. Key themes emerging from these studies are:

- the functional nature of drinking
- the importance of the buzz
- the importance of the drinking group, settings and local networks
- drinking as hedonism
- drinking as time out
- drinking as consumerism
- drinking as part of leisure
- drinking combined with illicit drug use
- the importance of boundaries in young people's lives.

Conclusions

1. Young people in Britain acquire adult drinking habits as part of normal socialisation. Youthful drinking is not deviant behaviour. Compared to the 1980s, in the 1990s, young people from the age of 11 up to young adults are drinking more alcohol, more frequently. Beverage choices have diversified in parallel with diversification of the drinks market. Gender differences are less among young people than in other age groups.

2. Within the framework of the government public health strategy, *Our Healthier Nation*, young people are an important target group for alcohol education and prevention of alcohol misuse, in order to address two of the four national priority areas, accidents and mental health.

3. Descriptive studies alone are insufficient to inform detailed health promotion interventions relevant to the needs of young people.

4. In England, public education about alcohol has so far largely been aimed at adults. Current alcohol education tends to use language, methods and messages that are framed by adults, for adults. Research to explore young people's interpretations of alcohol education messages would seem to be an important prerequisite for planning appropriate interventions.

5. Heavy sessional (binge) drinking patterns are particularly prevalent in young people. Alcohol education strategies aimed at young people need to acknowledge *why* young people get drunk and the part getting drunk plays in their social worlds. Further research is needed into the social norms for drunken behaviour among different ages and cultural groups of young people and the self-control strategies that young people adopt to limit their drinking.

6. We know relatively little about how drinking practices fit into adolescent social worlds, the meaning of drinking to different groups of young people of various ages and cultural backgrounds and the norms and rules that govern their drinking behaviour. The need to explore the place and meaning of drinking in young women's lives is a particular priority because it appears that gender differences in frequency and consumption may be diminishing. Another priority is to research more fully the needs of young people from different ethnic and religious groups.

7. The finding that risky drinking among young people is not confined to those who exceed adult sensible drinking levels, supports the argument for alcohol education aimed at all young people and not just those who are heavy drinkers.

8. Alcohol education initiatives will need to take into account the cultural, geographical, ethnic, religious and socio-demographic differences in young people's alcohol-related knowledge, attitudes and behaviour. This implies appropriate baseline research, with identified target groups of young people, before interventions are implemented. Parents and peer group cultures are also important target groups.

9. Within the *Our Healthier Nation* strategy, it is not what young people know about alcohol, but what they do with that knowledge that is important. Health educators might usefully consider not only what young

people need to know, but also why they need to know it. In seeking to reduce or minimise experience of alcohol-related harm and risk-taking by young people, it will be necessary not only to provide information but also to develop the cognitive skills which enable young people to use alcohol information.

Introduction

BACKGROUND: WERE RESEARCHERS EVER ADOLESCENTS?

Young people's drinking patently worries adults. In conducting this review, I have read many reports that describe youthful drinking as problematic, at risk, or antisocial. In describing what young people know, think and do about alcohol, I am left wondering whether alcohol researchers were ever young themselves. Perhaps they never experienced adolescence, metamorphosing overnight from children into fully developed, socially responsible adults? The moral panic about youthful drinking described by Dorn (1983) is evident in the way questions have been asked and the assumptions and interpretations made by many research studies on young people and alcohol. Many have focused on the problems related to young people's drinking and have labelled young drinkers as deviant. This is a particularly dominant paradigm in North American studies.

Recently, British researchers have challenged this perspective, arguing that adolescent drinking in Britain is essentially normal behaviour, which is part of the process of socialisation and reflects adult norms and drinking practices within the wider cultural setting (Sharp and Lowe, 1989; May, 1992; Lowe, Foxcroft and Sibley, 1993; Parker, 1995). Also, as studies of young people's illicit drug use (Davies and Coggans, 1991), and ethnographic studies of young people's drinking (Dorn, 1983; Gofton, 1990) have demonstrated, young people use alcohol for positive reasons, as they perceive them. This review will argue that, as Sharp and Lowe remark, seeing youthful drinking as inevitably problematic 'runs the risk of turning what is essentially normal behaviour into something deviant' (Sharp and Lowe, 1989, p. 305).

1

REVIEW REMIT

The Health Education Authority commissioned this review to inform those aspects of their alcohol education work that concern young people. The remit was to undertake a literature review that would explore:

- Young people's knowledge about alcohol.

- Young people's attitudes to alcohol. Specifically, their perceptions of alcohol advertising, alcohol in relation to self-image, perceptions of alcohol in relation to other priorities and health needs, gender and ethnic differences.

- Young people's drinking behaviour, particularly in the context of risk-taking and other drug use.

The age band set for the review was 11- to 24-year-olds, with the main interest in 11- to 20-year-olds.

The review concentrates on research published in English since 1980 and on data and research from the UK. Studies from elsewhere are included, if relevant to young people in the UK. Relevant material was identified by searching computerised databases, catalogues of specialist libraries and checking the references in recent relevant reviews and journal articles.

The main focus is on descriptive studies, examining young people's knowledge about alcohol, their attitudes, beliefs and expectancies and their drinking behaviour. The review does not cover (alcohol) prevention, education or treatment interventions with young people, nor does it include evaluative studies, which are the subject of a separate review (Foxcroft, Lister-Sharp and Lowe, 1997). Brief reference is made to the range of analytical studies that seek to explain young people's use of alcohol.

This review is divided into chapters that explore the main themes. Each chapter presents evidence on the theme and includes a summary. The final chapter brings together the conclusions and makes recommendations for action.

LIMITATIONS OF THE REVIEW

In examining a wide field of literature, the review has inevitably encountered problems of comparison, generalisability and relevance. The data presented here were derived from studies with differing epistemologies, theories, methods, respondents, data sources and methods of analysis. Studies were conducted in a wide range of social and cultural settings. In order to meet the HEA's requirements to produce a review that would be accessible to health promotion practitioners, detailed methodological critiques of the evidence are not given. Some specific difficulties encountered in examining the literature are given below.

- Much of the literature derives from North America and its relevance to young people in the UK is questionable, due to cultural differences, not only in young people's behaviour, but also the predominant assumption by researchers that *any* use of alcohol by young people is problematic. Under-age drinking in North America is actually illegal, whereas in the United Kingdom the situation is more ambiguous. There are legal restrictions on buying alcohol and on where young people can drink (i.e. not on licensed premises or in public places with local by-law restrictions) but drinking *per se* is not illegal for young people in the United Kingdom.

- There are no agreed definitions of 'young people'. In order to access information about the 11–24 age group, it was necessary to scrutinise literature referenced under 'children', 'adolescents', 'teenagers', 'young people' and 'young adults'. As they grow older, young people's drinking behaviour changes considerably; therefore the review usually states the age group included in different studies.

- There is a similar lack of uniformity over definitions of alcohol terminology such as 'heavy drinking', 'excessive drinking', 'binge drinking', 'alcohol problems' and 'alcoholism'. Definitions of binge drinking are discussed in the text.

- Stereotypical assumptions about the nature of youth and adolescence were common in the literature, as also found by Aggleton (1996) in a review of the literature on health promotion and young people. In-depth studies of small groups of young people reveal wide variations in drinking behaviour. As Aggleton points out, young people's experience of alcohol varies widely within and between societies and local communities: 'such variation is not random, but patterned and structured by factors such as age, social background, place of residence, gender and sexuality, ethnicity and above all by the material resources available. It is important to remember this in evaluating research findings on young people and health in order to avoid stereotyping people and their health needs.' (Aggleton, 1996, p. 9.)

• Milburn *et al.* (1995) draw attention to epistemological (theories of knowledge) differences in the research process. In the literature examined for this review, the positivist view predominated. This assumes that objective facts can be established about young people's social worlds, the emphasis being on statistically-based evidence and quantitative methods. Milburn *et al* note that this approach has underpinned much of the study of health behaviour in general. This review recognises that other theories of knowledge do exist and may have important contributions to make to our understanding of young people and alcohol. For example within the interpretivist perspective, young people's use of alcohol is viewed as being socially and culturally defined, rather than objective fact. The purpose of research is seen as exploring how young people understand and make sense of their worlds and the place and meaning of alcohol within it. Researchers adopting an interpretivist view commonly use qualitative methods. While recognising that there is continued debate about the validity and comparability of research derived from such differing perspectives, this review presents and acknowledges data derived from both ends of the epistemological spectrum.

• Accurately measuring young people's drinking behaviour is difficult. Some of the main reasons are summarised below.

Bias in self-reports. A comparison of self-reported consumption with estimates based on alcohol sales suggests that the self-report data tend towards under-reporting. Self-reported alcohol consumption accounts for about 40–60% of alcohol purchased (Midanik, 1982). However, studies comparing a variety of measures show high correlation levels between measures, supporting claims of reliability of self-report methods (Measham, 1996).

Drinking alcohol is such a commonplace activity, that people do not consciously keep track of their drinking habits, making profiling extremely difficult (Brain and Parker, 1997).

Lack of standardised questions and measures. Researchers have attempted to agree to ask the same kinds of questions and use the same measures, such as total weekly units consumed and/or units consumed on the last drinking occasion. However, these and other methodological differences mean that attempts to compare studies and thus identify continuities and changes in young people's drinking behaviour remain seriously restricted (Measham, 1996). For example, there are often discrepancies between answers to questions about 'drinking in the last seven days' and 'weekly drinking' because young people's drinking patterns are more varied and irregular than adults. Drinking in the last seven days will be recalled more accurately but may not be representative. Careful research such as Goddard's national surveys (Goddard 1996, 1997a, 1997b) and Measham's work in the North West of England (Measham, 1996) includes attempts to check whether 'last seven days' drinking is typical or not. More complex questions provide more valid and reliable answers, but this is offset against the length and complexity of the questionnaire and the risk of missing or invalid responses (Measham, 1996).

Limitations of surveys. Quantitative social surveys are the main method used to obtain data about young people's drinking behaviour. Household surveys where young people are interviewed at home tend to produce under-reporting compared with self-completion questionnaires at school (Brain and Parker, 1997). The style and presentation of the investigator can also bias the results (Coggans *et al.* 1991). Most surveys are school-based studies, which do not include non-attenders, whose drinking habits may vary considerably from those of other young people. As already argued, surveys are fairly crude techniques for identifying and describing the social contexts, meanings, norms and rituals attached to young people's drinking. For example, knowing how many units 14-year-old girls drank on their last drinking occasion is of limited value in informing a health education intervention, as it gives no information about the context of drinking. Therefore there is no way to judge whether the reported level of drinking is safe, sensible or appropriate.

Faulty recall is a problem because young people can often not remember how much they drank, especially if they shared a bottle or drank from non-standard containers. Exaggeration and/or under-reporting are also possible. Additionally, Brain and Parker (1997) note that numerous surveys have discounted questionnaires where respondents apparently have claimed to have drunk lethal amounts of alcohol.

Non-standard drinks. The settings where young people drink and diversification of the drinks market in the 1990s have created particular problems for measurement of alcohol consumption. Young people are increasingly consuming a wider range of new drinks of variable strengths in non-standard bottles and cans, which, in the absence of unit labelling, means that is very difficult for *them* to estimate their consumption accurately and even more difficult for researchers. The unit system is geared to pub drinking rather than the self-poured measures typically used by young people when drinking in places other than licensed premises.

1. Behaviour: What do young people do with alcohol?

SUMMARY

1. Accurate measurement of young people's alcohol consumption is difficult due to the bias inherent in self-reported behaviour, lack of standard questions and measures and young people's consumption of non-standard drinks. Measurement and classification of young people's alcohol consumption is not consistent between studies.

2. Prevalence of young people's alcohol consumption has been measured since the 1970s. Studies commonly involve single-phase, cross-sectional surveys. Continuing monitoring studies have recently been established.

3. Drinking alcohol begins at ages 8–12, with virtually all 12- to 14-year-olds having had some experience of drinking. However, the majority of young teenagers (11–16) do not drink regularly, and most of those who do drink, consume only small amounts.

4. Between the ages of 11 and 16, young people develop from taking the occasional sip of alcohol to being on the verge of drinking like adults; from drinking (mainly) under adult supervision to drinking independently.

5. There are different drinking patterns among schoolchildren in each of the four countries in the United Kingdom and there is considerable regional variation within countries. Direct comparison of data from different studies and countries is limited due to methodological differences. Schoolchildren's experience of drinking is least in Northern Ireland and greatest in Wales.

6. There is no clear evidence that young people are starting to drink earlier and the proportion of non-drinkers among 11- to 16-year-olds in England and Scotland has remained at about 40% for the last 20 years.

7.   Once they start to drink, young teenagers are drinking larger amounts, more frequently.

8.   Young teenagers are also increasingly involved in heavy sessional drinking or 'binge drinking'.

9.   Young teenage boys drink more alcohol than girls and they drink more frequently, a pattern that continues into adulthood. The frequency of girls' drinking is increasing at a faster rate than that of boys so that gender differences are diminishing.

10. Between the ages of 16 and 18, young people in England rapidly acquire adult drinking habits, in terms of drinking prevalence, consumption levels and settings for drinking. Mid-teens is the period when young people become experienced drinkers and drinking alcohol becomes the norm for the peer group.

11. There is no marked increase in drinking at 18, when it becomes legal to buy alcohol. Up to 16/17, there is no difference between the proportions of males and females who drink (although there are big differences in the amounts they drink). After 17 young men are more likely to be drinkers than young women; 16–18 is the peak age for young women's drinking in terms of frequency and quantity of alcohol consumed. For young men, consumption continues to rise and peaks at 18–21.

12. Young adults aged 18–24 are the heaviest drinking group in the population and their drinking is increasing. Four in ten males and one in five females in this age group are drinking above the weekly sensible drinking levels; 6% of young women drank over 35 units a week in 1996, twice the proportion recorded in 1994. Young women are the only population sector to show an increase in drinking at harmful levels.

13. Among adults, heavy sessional or 'binge drinking' is most prevalent among young adults aged 18–24, especially young men.

14. The majority of under-16s do *not* drink to excess. Consuming alcohol is normal behaviour across the older adolescent age group. Most

16-to 24-year-olds have been drunk and are involved in occasional heavy drinking sessions, although only a minority do so more frequently than once or twice a month.

15. There is little data on socio-economic and educational factors and young people's alcohol consumption. The picture is tentative and confusing, but suggests that 11- to 15-year-olds from better-off families who have low educational expectations are the group most likely to be frequent drinkers. Finance appears to be an important factor in accounting for variations in alcohol consumption among older teenagers. By their early 20s, it is individuals in the higher socio-economic groups who are more likely to be drinking at risky or unsafe levels.

16. Young people alter their drinking habits as their circumstances change or they enter different life stages. Students are more likely to drink above recommended weekly limits than their peers in the general population. Marriage or a stable relationship are important moderating influences on young men's drinking habits, which reduce even further when they become parents.

17. Generally, young people in England, Scotland and Wales are introduced to alcohol by their parents in the home, go on to drinking with friends in other places at around 13–14 years of age and begin to drink alcohol in pubs from the age of about 15 upwards.

18. Most under-18s who buy alcohol appear to be able to purchase it easily. A quarter of 11- to 16-year-olds have bought alcohol from an off-licence. There is no evidence that the extent of 'under-age' drinking in licensed premises has increased or decreased in the past 20 years. 'Under-age' drinking appears to be more prevalent in England than in the rest of the UK, and in England, both sexes are equally likely to drink in pubs 'under-age'.

19. Pubs, clubs and wine bars are the preferred setting for drinking for the 16–24 age group.

20. Following their introduction to drinking alcohol within the family, adolescents incorporate alcohol into their own social lives with their

friends. Drinking plays an important part in young people's leisure pursuits.

21. The majority of children up to the age of 12 prefer soft drinks to alcoholic beverages of any kind.

22. Diversification of the drinks market has targeted the youth sector, with a proliferation of new 'designer' drinks and 'alcopops', characterised by a relatively high %ABV. These have been incorporated into young people's drinking repertoire. The peak age for drinking alcopops is 13–16.

23. Sex differences in alcoholic beverage preferences are apparent even in novice drinkers aged under 16. Young people's beverage preferences are particularly susceptible to fashion and style influences and the new drinks exploit this.

24. Beverage choice is related to drunkenness. Drinking white cider and flavoured wines (both 'designer drinks') and vodka is related to drunkenness and binge drinking. Consumption of alcopops is not significantly related to drunkenness.

25. It has not been established whether the new drinks encourage more young people to start to drink, or existing drinkers to drink more, rather than simply influencing the beverage preferences of existing drinkers.

26. Young adults have been observed to consciously use alcohol as a mood altering drug and both seek and expect to get drunk, adopting drinking styles which achieve the best 'buzz', in the same way as users of illegal drugs.

27. Very little research has been done in Britain on ethnic and religious differences in young people's alcohol consumption. Among the 11–16 age group, African Caribbean and South Asian young people in the UK drink less than their white peers.

*

MEASURING AND MONITORING YOUNG PEOPLE'S DRINKING BEHAVIOUR: SOURCES OF DATA

Prevalence of alcohol consumption among the 10- to 24-year-old age group and particularly the under-20s, has been the subject of considerable research interest in the last 25 years. There have been several large-scale, single-phase, cross-sectional surveys of adolescent drinking using mainly quantitative methods (Davies and Stacey, 1972; McGuffin, 1979; Hawker, 1978; O'Connor, 1978; Plant, Peck and Samuel, 1985; Marsh, Dobbs and White, 1986; HEA/MORI, 1992a, 1992b; Goddard, 1991; Miller and Plant, 1996).

The above surveys are single phase and therefore most useful for describing young people's drinking at the particular point in time when the fieldwork was conducted. Trends over time are most reliably ascertained using time-series or multi-phase studies. Although trends in adult drinking habits have been monitored for some time via the General Household Survey, time-series studies of adolescent drinking have only been set up within the last ten years and the first published reports of these studies emerged in 1995–6. Since 1988, questions about drinking have been included in a biennial survey of smoking among secondary-school children in England and Scotland, enabling recent national drinking trends among 11- to 15-year-olds to be monitored (Goddard, 1996, 1997a, 1997b).

In Wales, the Welsh Youth Health Survey was set up in 1986 to collect data biennially on the health behaviour, including drug and alcohol use, of a national sample of secondary-school children.

Building on the HEA's survey *Tomorrow's Young Adults* (HEA/MORI, 1992b), the WHO European Office co-ordinates a collaborative cross-national study of the health behaviour of school-aged children (HBSC). This is carried out every four years. Scotland, Wales and Northern Ireland joined the survey group in 1992 and England joined in 1995. These studies provide health promotion monitoring indicators, including alcohol, for young people in the UK. The mandatory core protocol, which in future will facilitate cross-national comparisons, contains a small number of questions on alcohol. Participating countries can also opt to add special focus questions of their own. The reports published to date by the four national health promotion bodies do not facilitate inter-country comparisons within the UK, as the fieldwork dates are not yet synchronised and each has chosen to focus on different aspects of the data. Where possible, attempts are made within the text to draw comparisons.

Trends can also be identified from the large annual data sets collected by the University of Exeter, aggregated from primary and secondary schools completing their health-related behaviour questionnaires. However, these latter data sets are not nationally representative samples (Balding, 1994, 1995, 1996, 1997).

Within the UK, there have also been numerous local and regional studies of young people's drinking behaviour. Most are cross-sectional, single-phase survey studies, which produce data specific to the sampling area and time of sampling. These are useful for informing local interventions and to provide snapshots of what is happening at a certain time; indeed the level of regional variation suggests that they are preferable to national data for these purposes. However, due to methodological differences, they are usually not generalisable to young people elsewhere and they sometimes incorporate design errors that could have been avoided if a thorough literature study had been done beforehand (see preceding discussion on limitations of published research). Furthermore, few of the United Kingdom national surveys of young people's drinking give regional variations so, when looking at local studies, it is hard to know what is genuine local variation and what is due to different methodology. It is also difficult to see if young people's regional variation matches adult regional variation.

During the last decade, there has been a proliferation of local or regional lifestyle surveys, repeated at intervals and therefore useful to monitor change. Many include a few questions on alcohol use. Most involve samples of less than 500 respondents although a few involve huge data sets, for example the West Midlands Young People's Lifestyle Survey collected information from over 27,000 secondary-school children (Sherrat, MacArthur and Cheng, 1997). Because they provide local data, such surveys can often be more useful to service providers and planners than the national surveys. However, methodological differences between local surveys, particularly the way the questions are framed, mean that limited comparisons can be made between different local or regional surveys.

Adult drinking in Great Britain is monitored biannually by the Office for National Statistics (ONS) (formerly the Office of Population Censuses and Surveys (OPCS)) in the General Household Survey. The age group 16–24 has recently been adopted as the lower age band in this and other surveys of the adult population, reflecting the reality that the drinking habits of 16- to 18-year-olds closely resemble those of adults (OPCS, 1991, 1994; Bennett *et al.*,1996). To supplement the General Household Survey, since 1990, the Health Survey for England has offered another national source of annual data on adults' drinking. In 1995 and 1996 it included a sub-sample of young people aged 8–15. Young people were interviewed in the presence of parents, which probably explains lower figures obtained from these surveys than others (Prescott-Clarke and Primatesta, 1997).

SENSIBLE DRINKING

In the absence of any authoritative guidance on safe/risky consumption levels for adolescents, research reports usually discuss young people's alcohol consumption in relation to the Department of Health guidelines on *adult* sensible drinking. For all work published before 1996 (i.e. the bulk of work reported here), the sensible drinking message was that drinking less than 21 units per week for men and 14 units per week for women is unlikely to damage health (Lord Presidents' Report, 1991; Department of Health, 1992). In December 1995, the Department of Health issued new and more extensive guidance, which included an emphasis on daily rather than weekly consumption, in order to focus on binge drinking and drunkenness. The daily benchmarks, beyond which health risks occur, are considered to be 3–4 units per day for men and 2–3 units per day for women. Consistently drinking 4 units a day (men) or 3 units a day (women) is not advised. Unless specified, this report refers to the pre-1996 weekly levels for adult sensible drinking as they were the standards used by the research studies. The most recent data presented here discuss young people's drinking in terms of single drinking episodes, in line with current advice.

In the absence of authoritative guidance on safe/risky consumption levels for adolescents, researchers have varied in the way they have classified young peoples drinking as 'low', 'moderate', 'heavy', 'excessive', etc. For example, a survey of schoolchildren in England, aged 14–16, by Plant *et al.* (1990) found that 70% of boys and 78% of girls reported having drunk no more than 4 units on their last drinking occasion. The authors regard this level of drinking as 'moderate'. Without detailed information about the respondents' weight, tolerance and previous experience of drinking or information about the setting for drinking, it is a questionable use of the term 'moderate'. For example, drinking 4 units (2 pints of beer) over one hour would raise the blood alcohol level in any person weighting less than 8 stone and in all women, to above the legally permitted limit for driving.

Plant, Bagnall and Foster (1990) classified as 'heavy drinkers', young males who had consumed 11 units or more on their last drinking occasion, and young females who had consumed 8 units or more. In their sample of 14- to 16-year-olds, 10% of boys and 5% of girls were 'heavy drinkers'. The proportion rose rapidly with age (Table 1).

Table 1 'Heavy drinking' among English teenagers aged 14–16 (N = 5605)

Age	Males	Females
	%	%
14	5.4	7.1
15	10.7	10.1
16	13.5	15.5

Source: Plant, Bagnall and Foster (1990)

This definition of 'heavy drinking' is questionable for the same reasons as those applied to the term 'moderate'. Similarly, applying adult sensible drinking levels to young people's consumption levels may underestimate the proportions of young drinkers who are harming themselves or others.

HOW MANY YOUNG PEOPLE DRINK AND HOW MUCH DO THEY DRINK?

Continuity and change

During the 1970s and 1980s, studies of young people's alcohol consumption showed remarkable stability in drinking patterns (Marsh, Dobbs and White, 1986; Goddard, 1991). Reviews of research undertaken during this period concluded that there had been little change in patterns of alcohol use and no evidence that young people were drinking more (May, 1992; Lister-Sharp, 1994; Sharp and Lowe, 1989). In comparison, young people's drinking patterns in the 1990s exhibit both 'continuity and change' (Brain and Parker, 1997). There is still no clear evidence that children are starting to drink earlier, most young teenagers continue to drink modest amounts, infrequently and a minority of young people drink to excess and experience problems. The four changes identified by Brain and Parker (1997) are:

- major changes in the alcoholic drinks consumed by young people

- a possible increase in the proportion of non-drinkers and light drinkers among the 16–25 age group

- weekly young drinkers are drinking more

- regular young drinkers are drinking more alcohol per session.

There is also evidence that more young people are drinking regularly, i.e. at least once a week (Goddard, 1997a; Roberts *et al.*, 1997). These trends and other recent changes in young people's alcohol will now be discussed.

Children aged 11 and under

Growing up with alcohol

Young people's experience of alcohol begins well before they reach their teens, as a normal part of socialisation within the home. Ninety per cent of adult drinkers drink at home, and half do so at least once a week (HEA/RSGB, 1991). Most children's first experience of alcohol will be gained from observing the drinking behaviour of family members. By the time they are 10 years of age, children can distinguish alcoholic drinks by container, smell and appearance and can accurately describe the effect of drinking on behaviour (Jahoda and Crammond, 1972; Fossey, 1992, 1994).

Starting to drink

Walker (1997) points out that it is not easy for young people to pinpoint the actual age when they first try alcohol. Recall of the event is often vague and as children get older, their definition of a 'proper drink' changes. All of the large-scale studies cited earlier have indicated that drinking begins at ages 8–12, with virtually all 12- to 14-year-olds having had some experience of drinking. For example, in 1991–2, only 15% of boys and 20% of girls aged 8–9 who completed the University of Exeter's health-related behaviour questionnaire had not yet sampled an alcoholic drink (Balding and Shelley, 1993). Consumption patterns for the health-related behaviour questionnaire respondents in the following two years, 1993–5, confirm that by the time they complete primary school (year 6, 10–11 years) most children will have had some limited experience of drinking alcohol, though very few will drink regularly (Balding, 1996).

Data from national monitoring surveys for England and Scotland suggest that age of initiation seems to have remained fairly constant in these countries over the last 20 years (Goddard, 1997a, 1997b). One local, comparative study found evidence of delayed onset of alcohol use among young teenagers in Humberside in 1992 compared with a 1988 baseline. This change was particularly apparent in boys (Foxcroft, Lowe and Lister-Sharp, 1995). More recently, over the decade 1986–1996, the Welsh biennial Youth Health Surveys also found delayed onset of use in boys, but no significant change in girls. In 1986, 89.1% of 11- to 12-year-olds had ever tasted alcohol; ten years later the proportion had fallen to 81.4% of 11- to 12-year-olds (Roberts *et al.*, 1997). Data from a longer time-series is needed to discover the direction and stability of any trend in onset of use.

The potential risks attached to such youthful drinking are considerable. By virtue of their small size, inexperience and immaturity, children will become intoxicated after only one or two units of alcohol. The threshold for experiencing severe alcohol poisoning, and even death, will also be very low.

Young teenagers (11–16)

The early teenage years are an important period of change for many aspects of young people's lives, including their drinking behaviour. Between the ages of 11 and 16, young people develop from taking the occasional sip of alcohol to being on the verge of drinking like adults; from drinking (mainly) under adult supervision to drinking independently.

There are different drinking patterns among schoolchildren in each of the four countries in the United Kingdom. Direct comparison of data from different studies and countries is limited due to the methodological differences discussed earlier. Data from each country are presented, followed by a discussion of trends and some inter-country comparisons.

Young teenagers in England

The proportion of 11- to 15-year-olds in England who don't drink at all has remained at about 40% since the early 1980s (Balding, 1997; Goddard, 1996, 1997a). In 1996, Goddard's national survey of secondary-school children in England and Scotland described the usual drinking behaviour of most 11- to 15-year-olds as 'relatively modest' (Goddard, 1997a, p. 20); even amongst the oldest pupils, most drank no more than once a week.

An HEA national survey of 11- to 15-year-old schoolchildren in England conducted in 1993–4 (Turtle, Jones and Hickman, 1997) found that 23% did not drink at all and 53% described their drinking as 'hardly drink alcohol' or 'drink only a little'.

Since biennial, national surveys by ONS of 11- to 15-year-old schoolchildren began in 1988, there has been a fairly marked increase in drinking frequency among young adolescent drinkers in England. From 1988 to 1996, the proportion of 11- to 15-year-olds who had had a drink in the previous week rose by over a third, from 20% to 27% (Goddard, 1997a).

Although average weekly alcohol consumption in this age group is low (1.8 units in 1996) it has more than doubled since 1988 (0.8 units). Among those who had drunk alcohol in the previous week, the average number of units consumed rose from 5.4 units in 1990 to 8.4 in 1996. The rise in consumption in 1996 was statistically significant in pupils aged 13–15. It was partly due to increased frequency of drinking, but also to increased consumption among young drinkers. The proportion of 11- to 15-year-olds who had drunk 15 units or more rose from just 1% in 1990 to 4 % in 1996.

Comparing the ONS survey data for England from 1994 and 1996, the trend towards increased consumption is particularly apparent in 15 year-old drinkers. Boys' consumption in the previous week increased by 47%, from 8.8 units to 12.9 units, while girls' consumption increased by 21% from 6.6 units in 1994 to 8 units in 1996. In 1996, one-third of 15-year-old boys who had drunk alcohol last week (15% of all 15-year-olds) had drunk 15 units or more in the week (Goddard, 1997a, p. 9).

Young teenagers in Scotland

In Scotland, there has been a small increase in the 1990s in the proportion of children aged 12–15 who drink alcohol at all, from 59% in 1990 to 64% in 1996. There has been a more marked increase in the amount drunk by those who do drink, paralleling the findings for schoolchildren in England. From 1990 to 1996, Scotland saw a two-thirds increase in the proportion of 12- to 15-year-olds who had had a drink in the previous week, from 14% to 23% (Goddard, 1997a).

As in England, average weekly alcohol consumption (based on all children including non-drinkers) has more than doubled, from 0.8 units in 1988 to 1.9 units in 1996. In Scotland in 1996, those who did drink, drank significantly more than their peers in England. The average number of units consumed by drinkers in the previous week was 11.1 in Scotland compared with 8.4 in England. Goddard advises that, as for schoolchildren in England, these averages conceal a wide variation in the amounts young teenagers drink. The overwhelming majority had drunk little or no alcohol in the previous week, and most of the remainder had drunk only modest amounts. At the other extreme of the scale, 5% of boys and 3% of girls had drunk 15 units or more in the previous week.

Young teenagers in Wales

The main sources of national drinking trends for young teenagers in Wales are the biennial national HBSC studies conducted since 1986 and the ONS biennial, cross-national surveys, conducted in 1990, 1992 and 1994 (Goddard, 1996). The 1996 ONS survey, reported above, only includes Scotland and England (Goddard, 1997a).

In 1994, just under two-fifths (37%) of all 11- to 15-year-olds said they never drank alcohol, 27% drank a few times a year, 17% once or twice a month and 19% at least once a week (Goddard, 1996). As with other countries, the proportions drinking increased sharply with age, rising from 27% of 11-year-olds to 90% of 15-year-olds – over a third (38%) of 15-year-olds said they drank every week. Those who had drunk alcohol in the previous week had consumed only modest amounts – 7.4 units on average, and a quarter had drunk less than 2 units. However, 12% (2% of all pupils) had drunk 15 units or more, as had 22% of 15-year-old boys (10% of all 15-year-old boys).

Over the period 1990–1994, the ONS surveys recorded little change in the proportion of 11- to 15-year-olds who drank alcohol at all (63% in 1994) but quite a marked increase in frequency of drinking. The proportion of pupils who said they usually drank every week increased from 15% in 1990 to 19% in 1994. This increase was more apparent in boys (23% in 1990 to 28% in 1994) than in girls (22% in both years).

This increased frequency of drinking by boys was accompanied by an increase in the amount drunk in the last week, from an average of 1.3 units per pupil in 1990 to 1.8 units in 1994 (including non-drinkers). Among those who had drunk alcohol in the previous week, the increases in consumption was greater for girls (from 5.2 units in 1990 to 6.3 units in 1994) than for boys (8.3 units in 1990 to 8.5 units in 1994).

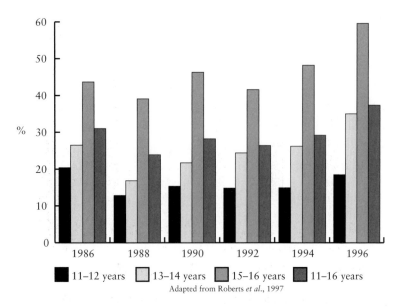

Adapted from Roberts *et al.*, 1997

Figure 1 Weekly drinking by 11- to 16-year-olds in Wales (%)

The alcohol variables reported by the Welsh biennial HBSC study are: ever tasted alcohol, drinking alcohol at least weekly and being drunk four or more times. Overall consumption, in terms of average units, is not reported; respondents are asked how frequently they consume different types of alcoholic beverage (Roberts *et al.*, 1997, Roberts, Blakey and Tudor-Smith, 1997). The proportion of 11- to 16-year-olds reporting having ever tasted alcohol has remained relatively stable over the decade 1986–96, at 93.4% in 1986 and 92.1% in 1996. However, as also noted by the ONS surveys, weekly alcohol consumption has risen sharply over this time period, particularly among 13- to 16-year-olds. As Figure 1 shows, across the whole age range 11–16, the percentage of who drink alcohol at least weekly rose from 31% in 1986 to 38% in 1996, while weekly drinking increased from 27% to 35% for 13- to 14-year-olds and from 44% to 60% for 15- to 16-year-olds.

The proportions of 11- to 16-year-olds reporting having been drunk on four or more occasions also rose over the decade, among all age-sex groups except 11- to 12-year-old boys. The increase was particularly marked among older boys and girls, as shown in Figure 2. The percentage

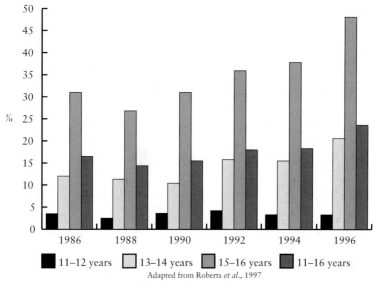

Adapted from Roberts *et al.*, 1997

Figure 2 11- to 16-year-olds in Wales drunk 4 or more times (%)

of 15- to 16-year-olds who have been drunk four or more times rose from 31% in 1986 to 48% in 1996.

The HBSC surveys also reveal trends in consumption of different alcoholic beverages (Roberts, Blakey and Tudor-Smith, 1997). Over the whole age group (11–16) weekly consumption of cider, beer, wine and spirits did not change significantly during the decade 1986–96, with the exception of beer drinking among girls which increased from 11% to 13% and a reduction in wine drinking among boys, from 14% to 9%. Analysis by age group revealed significant increases in weekly beer/lager and cider consumption among 15- to 16-year-olds of both sexes, as shown in Table 2.

Table 2 Percentage drinking beer/lager and cider weekly, 15- to 16-year-olds, Wales, 1986 and 1996

	Beer/lager weekly			Cider weekly		
	Male	Female	Both sexes	Male	Female	Both sexes
1986	39	19	30	18	17	17
1996	54	27	41	22	23	22

Source: Roberts, Blakey and Tudor-Smith, 1997

21

Conversely, weekly cider drinking in younger schoolchildren declined over the decade. In 1986, 18% of 11- to 12-year-old boys and 8% of girls reported drinking cider weekly, by 1996, these proportions were 8% and 3%.

Young teenagers in Northern Ireland

Recent national data on young teenagers and alcohol in Northern Ireland can be derived from national surveys of adolescent smoking and drinking conducted in 1988 and 1990 and from national HBSC studies conducted in 1992 and 1994 (HPANI, 1994,1995). Although the age group sampled (11–15) was the same, limited comparisons can be made between the two types of studies owing to methodological differences, particularly the wording of questions. The published data from the HBSC studies are limited in comparison to the level of detail provided by the parallel HBSC reports from England and Wales; the Health Promotion Agency for Northern Ireland intends to address this problem in their 1996 HBSC study.

In Northern Ireland, compared to other parts of the UK, greater proportions of secondary-school children do not drink at all or only very occasionally. Twenty years ago, a survey by McGuffin (1979) of 11- to 16-year-olds noted high levels of both abstinence and heavy drinking, a reflection of Northern Ireland's adult drinking pattern. In 1988 and 1990, national surveys of adolescent smoking and drinking, while noting a continuing polarisation, also identified increasing proportions of drinkers (DHSS Northern Ireland, 1989; Craig, Francis and McWhirter, 1991). Both surveys found that young teenagers who did drink were more likely than their peers in the rest of the UK to drink more than adult recommended weekly limits. Loretto (1994) also noted similar polarised patterns in a comparative study of young people's drinking habits in Northern Ireland and Scotland.

From a consistently lower base than the rest of the UK in the 1980s, the proportion of drinkers and frequent drinkers among 11- to 15-year-olds in Northern Ireland has dramatically increased in the 1990s. In 1988, 37% of this age group drank alcohol (defined as a proper drink and more than just a sip), which was considerably lower than their peers in the rest of the UK. Nine per cent drank at least once a week (DHSS Northern

Ireland, 1989). In 1990, the proportion of drinkers was the same and 10% drank at least weekly (Craig, Francis and McWhirter, 1991). In 1994, the HBSC survey found that 52% had taken a 'whole drink' while almost 13% drank alcohol at least weekly (HPANI, 1995).

As in the rest of the UK, experience of alcohol increases with age; in 1994, 60% of 11- to 12-year-olds, 80% of 13- to 14-year-olds and 90% of 15- to 16-year-olds had tasted alcohol; 15- to 16-year-olds are six times more likely than 11- to 12-year-olds to drink alcohol at least weekly (HPANI, 1995).

Trends

By the time they reach 16, virtually all teenagers (94%) throughout the UK have had some experience of drinking alcohol (Miller and Plant, 1996). However, it should be noted that many young teenagers either do not drink alcohol at all, or drink small amounts, infrequently.

In the 1990s, the proportions of young teenagers who drink has increased in Scotland and Northern Ireland and has remained fairly stable in England and Wales. Once they start to drink, young adolescents are consuming larger amounts and are drinking more frequently. This trend has been observed in England (Goddard, 1997a), Scotland (Goddard, 1997b) and Wales (Roberts *et al.*, 1997), while increased frequency of drinking has been observed among schoolchildren in Northern Ireland (HPANI, 1995). All of these studies are based on data from large, nationally representative samples of schoolchildren.

The ONS cross-national study (Goddard, 1996) conducted in 1994 permits some comparisons between the drinking of schoolchildren in England, Scotland and Wales. Comparisons between countries should be treated with caution: the Scottish education system is different, so the age distribution covered in Scotland is not the same as in the other two countries. Table 3 summarises the main results. The proportion of 11- to 15-year-olds who drank during the previous week was significantly lower in Scotland than in England and Wales. However, in Scotland (and in Wales to a lesser extent), those who did drink drank significantly more than their English counterparts. These differences applied to both sexes.

Average consumption per pupil was similar in all three countries. The types of alcohol drunk were similar for England and Wales, but in Scotland young drinkers were more likely to drink spirits.

Table 3 Schoolchildren's drinking in 1994, comparison of England, Wales and Scotland

	England (Age 11–15)	Wales (Age 11–15)	Scotland (Age 12–15)
Percentage of pupils who drank last week			
Boys	26	28	21
Girls	22	22	19
Total	24	25	20
Average units drunk last week per pupil			
Boys	1.5	1.8	1.6
Girls	1.0	1.1	1.0
Total	1.3	1.5	1.3
Percentage of pupils who had drunk each type of drink			
Beer, lager, cider	18	20	14
Shandy	6	6	3
Wine	11	11	10
Martini, sherry	3	3	4
Spirits, liqueurs	9	9	11
Average units drunk last week per drinker			
Boys	7.4	8.5	10.6
Girls	5.4	6.3	6.9
Total	6.4	7.4	8.7
Percentage of drinkers who had drunk each type of drink			
Beer, lager, cider	76	80	70
Shandy	24	26	16
Wine	48	44	51
Martini, sherry	15	14	20
Spirits, liqueurs	39	39	60

Source: Goddard (1996), p. 38

Differences between countries in the UK were also identified in a UK-wide survey of 15- to 16-year-old schoolchildren's drinking, smoking and drug use conducted in 1995 (Miller and Plant, 1996). This study found that experience of drinking was highest in Wales and lowest in Northern Ireland. These results should be treated with caution, as the sample sizes for Wales (n = 166) and Northern Ireland (n = 328) were small.

Gender differences

The most recent ONS and HBSC surveys cited above identify gender differences, in the amount and frequency of young adolescents' alcohol consumption, which were not apparent in earlier studies. For example in 1989, *Tomorrow's Young Adults*, the HEA lifestyle survey of schoolchildren in England (HEA/MORI, 1992b) found little difference between the alcohol consumption levels of boys and girls aged 9–15 in England.

In the 1996 ONS survey (Goddard, 1997a), in England, mean consumption per drinker was higher for boys, at 9.7 units in the past week, compared with 7 units for girls. Boys were also twice as likely to have drunk 15 units or more. In Scotland in 1996, girls were less likely than boys to drink at all, but among those girls who did drink, average consumption levels were not much lower than boys' (10 units for girls and 11.9 for boys).

In both Scotland and England, the frequency of girls' drinking is increasing at a faster rate than that of boys, so that gender differences are diminishing. In contrast with earlier surveys in the ONS series, which found that boys were more likely than girls to have had a drink in the past week, the 1996 survey for 11- to 15-year-olds in England recorded little gender difference in drinking frequency. Twenty seven per cent of boys and 26% of girls had had a drink in the past week. From 1988 to 1996, drinking in the past week by 11- to 15-year-old girls increased from 17% to 26%, and by 15 year old girls from 36% to 55%. The comparable increases for boys were much less: from 24% to 27% for 11- to 15-year-olds and from 45% to 50% for 15-year-olds.

In Scotland in 1996, 24% of boys aged 12–15 and 21% of girls had had a drink in the past week. Over the four years 1990–1994, the proportion of 12- to 15-year-old girls in Scotland who reported drinking in the past week had increased by 75%, from 12% to 21%. Drinking in the past week by boys increased by 50% over the same period, from 16% in 1990 to 24% in 1996.

In Northern Ireland, gender differences are considerable; in 1994, at all ages 11–15, boys were more likely than girls to have tasted alcohol, to be current drinkers and to have been drunk. In 1992, 33% of 11- to 15-year-old boys and 18% of girls drank alcohol at least weekly (HPANI, 1995).

Regional differences

Within the broad national patterns and trends described above, young teenagers' alcohol consumption shows considerable local and regional variation. For example, in 1989, *Tomorrow's Young Adults* (HEA/MORI, 1992b) found that frequency of alcohol consumption in 9–16s was particularly high in the South West of England, Yorkshire and Humberside (36% drank 'last week') and low in the West Midlands (28% drank last week) and Inner London (27%). Drinking more than the sensible adult weekly levels (14 and 21 units) was more common in Outer London (7%), the South West and the North West (6%).

In contrast, in 1991, a study of 14- to 15-year-olds in the North West of England found a slightly lower rate of current and recent drinking particularly amongst girls, compared with national rates (Newcombe, Measham and Parker, 1995).

The West Midlands Young People's Lifestyle survey (Sherrat, MacArthur and Cheng, 1997) obtained data on alcohol use from a representative sample of over 27,000 pupils in years 7, 9 and 11 (11–16 years). This survey found that 27% of the overall sample were weekly drinkers. Frequency of alcohol consumption increased with age; 11% of 11- to 12-year-olds drank weekly, rising to 48% of 15- to 16-year-olds. Amongst weekly drinkers, the average number of units consumed in a week was 12.

Several other local studies in England have found that about half of 15-year-olds are drinking alcohol at least weekly: a survey of alcohol purchase and use by 14- and 15-year-olds from three schools in Hambleton and Richmond, North Yorkshire (Flanagan, 1997); a young people-led survey in Burslem, Staffordshire (Staffordshire Police, 1997) and a survey of young people's drinking in Fenland (Drinksense, 1996).

Drunkenness and binge drinking

The lack of consensus on binge drinking referred to in the discussion of the limitations of the review (see Introduction) includes differences in public and professional understandings as well as technical arguments about how much alcohol over what time period (ICAP, 1997). The popular interpretation of a binge is that of staying drunk for days at a time. The clinical definition is similar – continuous, dependent drinking over a day or more until the drinker is unconscious. In this review, binge drinking is taken as meaning drinking a lot of alcohol in a single session of drinking. The HEA tends to avoid definitions of binge drinking in terms of units per session in its publicity because public interpretations of the phrase vary. Its value to researchers lies in its use as a measure of risk of alcohol-related harm, which recognises that most of the short-term harm linked with alcohol is from single episodes of drunkenness, rather than drinking more than the safe weekly levels, or individual daily drinking (Department of Health, 1995). This applies to adults' drinking as well as young people's. Definitions of the amount of alcohol consumed in a binge vary; many (but not all) North American studies use five or more drinks in a row for men and four for women. Definitions of binge drinking in UK studies tend to be higher and are not consistent between studies; attempts to scale down definitions of adult binge drinking to produce something meaningful for young people are even more variable. A recent survey commissioned by the HEA used 8 or more units in a single session for men, and 6 or more units in a single session for women, as a definition of a heavy drinking occasion in adults, aged 16+ (Rowlands, 1998).

Despite the lack of consensus on definitions of binge drinking, this seems to be a pattern common among young people throughout the developed world (ICAP, 1997), although it is not so commonly recorded in the under-16 age group.

Taking into account differences in definitions and measurement, the trend towards increased frequency of drinking and increased alcohol consumption among young teenage drinkers in the UK does appear to be accompanied by increased intoxication and binge drinking. Data from the UK countries' HBSC studies report varying proportions of 11- to 16-year-olds who have experienced intoxication. In Northern Ireland in 1992, almost 40% of young drinkers had been drunk and a quarter of those who had ever tasted alcohol had been drunk more than once (HPANI, 1992). In England in 1995, 55% of current drinkers had been drunk at least once and 17% had been drunk four or more times (19% of boys and 15% of girls). In Scotland in 1994, a slightly higher proportion of 11- to 15-year-olds (14%) had been drunk four or more times than in 1990 (13%), with a statistically significant increase among 15-year-olds. One-quarter of boys in this age group had been drunk four times or more in 1990, rising to over a third (35%) in 1994. The same measure of intoxication had almost doubled for girls, from 17% in 1990 to 30% in 1994. Ten years of data from the Welsh HBSC surveys, from 1986 to 1996, also indicate a trend towards increased experience of intoxication. The percentage of 11- to 16-year-olds who reported having been drunk four or more times increased in boys by one-third, from 20% to 26%, and by over two-thirds in girls, from 13% to 22%. (Roberts *et al.*, 1997). The latest data for England, Scotland and Wales suggest relatively little gender difference in experience of intoxication. Drunkenness is more common among boys than girls in Northern Ireland (HPANI, 1992).

Miller and Plant (1996) also identified country differences in binge drinking and intoxication among 15- to 16-year-old schoolchildren in the UK. Intoxication and binge drinking (the latter was defined as more than 5 units on one occasion) were lowest in Northern Ireland and highest in Wales. These results should be treated with caution, as the sample sizes for Northern Ireland and Wales were small and may not be representative of national drinking patterns. This study found that by the time they reached 16, most teenagers (80%) had been intoxicated (nearly half in the previous month) and about half had been binge drinking in the previous month.

A longitudinal cohort study of 14- to 16-year-olds in the North West of England also reported that young teenagers were increasingly involved in 'binge drinking', consuming a larger quantity of alcohol in a single session. In 1991, at the age of 14, one in four drinkers reported consuming over 10 units of alcohol on their last drinking occasion. In 1992, at age 15, one in three drinkers reported drinking over 10 units (Measham, 1996). The researchers suggested that this may be due to regional variations and the tradition of heavy drinking in the North West, and also to the changing types of alcoholic beverages marketed by the drinks industry (Newcombe, Measham, and Parker, 1995; Measham 1996). The consumption of 'designer drinks' and 'alcopops' is discussed below under 'Beverage preferences: What do young people choose to drink?'

Young people aged 16–18

Between ages of 16 and 18, young people in England rapidly acquire adult drinking habits, in terms of drinking prevalence, consumption levels and settings for drinking. Mid-teens is the period when young people become experienced drinkers and drinking alcohol becomes the norm for the peer group. Drinking becomes seen as a sociable and 'adult' activity. It is evident that long before the age of 18, when they can legally buy alcohol or drink it in a licensed bar, the majority of young people are drinking on regular basis.

A 1991 survey of drinking habits in England and Wales (Goddard, 1991) recorded consumption levels in relation to the former limits for adult 'sensible' drinking (females, 14 units/week, males 21 units/week) and the upper risky/harmful drinking threshold (females 35 units/week, males 50 units/week). Among 16- to 17-year-olds, 13% of boys and 8% of girls were already drinking more than the sensible limits, while 2% of boys and 1% of girls aged 16–17 consumed more than the harmful limits, which are considered to predict serious health damage.

Today's Young Adults, an HEA survey of the health and lifestyles of 16- to 19-year-olds in England, conducted in 1990, provides the most comprehensive picture of drinking prevalence in this age group (HEA/MORI, 1992a). However, drinking patterns in 16–19s may have already changed since 1990, or currently be in the process of changing towards increased frequency of drinking and increased amounts of alcohol consumed, following the trends reported for younger teenagers. If the cohort of young teenagers continues to drink in the same way as they mature, then the 16–19 age group could be moving into riskier drinking patterns (i.e. binge drinking), with females narrowing the gap on males in terms of frequency of drinking.

The HEA survey confirmed that the vast majority of young people over the age of 16 see themselves as drinkers. Sixty-one per cent of 16–19s reported having had a drink last week, 52% classified themselves as regular drinkers, 24% as occasional drinkers and 21% as rare drinkers. Only 3% described themselves as non-drinkers.

Recent surveys have shown that there is no marked increase in drinking at 18, when it becomes legal to buy alcohol. The General Household Survey, which provides the most comprehensive source of national drinking patterns among adults, now recognises this by including 16-year-olds as the lower age limit for respondents (trends in General Household Survey data are described below). Up to 16/17, there is little difference between the proportions of males and females who drink (although there are big differences in the amounts they drink). After 17, young men are more likely to be drinkers than young women; 16–18 is the peak age for young women's drinking in terms of frequency and quantity of alcohol consumed (Plant, Peck and Samuel, 1985; Plant *et al.*, 1990; Goddard, 1992; HEA/MORI, 1992a, 1992b). For young men, consumption continues to rise and peaks at 18–21.

Young adults (18–24)

Young adults' drinking is monitored biannually via the General Household Survey, which interviews about 17,000 adults each year in England, Scotland and Wales. Questions on drinking habits have been asked in alternate years since 1984. For consistency, the survey continues to measure drinking in weekly, rather than daily amounts and uses the former sensible drinking levels of 21 and 14 units per week. It defines heavy drinkers as men drinking over 50 units per week and women drinking over 35 units per week, the levels regarded as harmful.

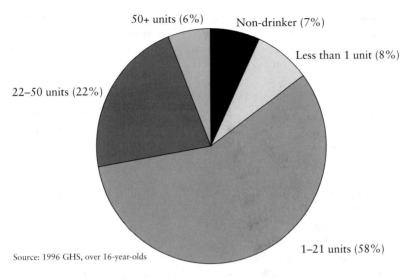

Source: 1996 GHS, over 16-year-olds

Figure 3 Men's drinking, weekly amounts

Young adults aged 18–24 are the heaviest drinking group in the population and they are drinking more (ONS, 1997a, 1998). The proportion of men in the whole adult population of Great Britain who are drinking more than the former sensible limits (21 units per week) has remained fairly steady since 1986, whereas the trend for young men has been more erratic (Table 4). In 1996, 41% of 18- to 24-year-olds drank over 21 units per week, the highest level recorded since 1984. If 16- and 17-year-olds are included, 35% of 16- to 24-year-old males drank over 21 units per week. Average weekly consumption for 16- to 24-year-old males was 20.3 units per week, compared with 19.1 units in 1992. (Figures 3 and 4.)

Table 4 Percentage of 18- to 24-year-olds drinking more than sensible weekly limits (14 units for females, 21 units for males)

	1984	1986	1988	1990	1992	1994	1996
	%	%	%	%	%	%	%
18–24 males	35	39	35	36	38	35	41
18–24 females	15	19	17	18	18	23	24
All adult males	25	27	27	28	27	27	27
All adult females	9	10	10	11	11	13	14

Source: General Household Survey reports

31

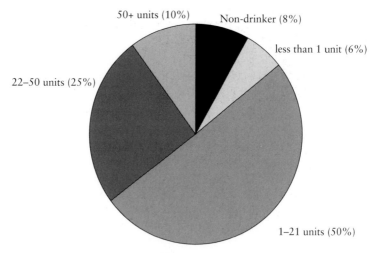

50+ units (10%)

Non-drinker (8%)

less than 1 unit (6%)

22–50 units (25%)

1–21 units (50%)

Source: 1996 GHS, 16- to 24-year-olds

Figure 4 Young men's drinking, weekly amounts

The proportion of all adult women drinking more than sensible weekly limits (14 units per week) has slowly risen since 1984, across all age groups, and this upward trend, although again erratic, is particularly apparent among young women. The 1996 figures (ONS, 1998) reveal that 21% of 16- to 24-year-old women and 24%, nearly a quarter, of 18- to 24-year-olds are drinking above the former sensible drinking limits. This is a much higher proportion than other age groups of women (14% of all adult women in 1996 drank more than 14 units per week). Average consumption for 16- to 24-year-old women was 9.5 units per week in 1996, compared to 7.3 units in 1992. (Figures 5 and 6.)

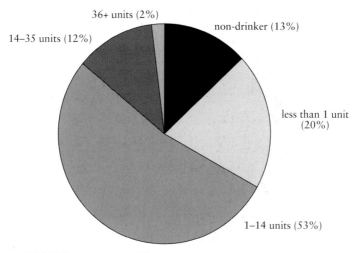

Source: 1996 GHS, over 16-year-olds

Figure 5 Women's drinking, weekly amounts

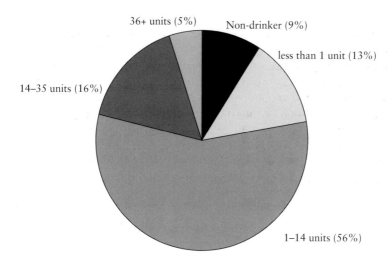

Source: 1996 GHS, 16- to 24-year-olds

Figure 6 Young women's drinking, weekly amounts

Heavy drinkers, getting drunk and binge drinking

Young adults are more likely than other ages to be heavy drinkers, both in terms of weekly drinking at harmful levels and single heavy drinking occasions (binge drinking). In 1996, 12% of young men aged 18–24 drank 50 units per week, twice as high as all adult males (6%), but no higher than in previous years. In contrast, young women are the only sector of the adult population to show an increase in drinking at harmful levels. In 1996, 6% of young women aged 18–24 drank over 35 units a week, compared with 2% of all adult women. This is twice the level recorded for young women in 1994 (ONS, 1998).

Preliminary findings of a national survey of adults in England in 1997, conducted by ONS for the HEA (Goddard, 1998) indicate that young adults aged 16–24 are much more likely to indulge in heavy drinking sessions than other adult age groups. Rather than risk the ambiguity inherent in the term 'binge drinking' this survey focuses on 'heavy drinking occasions', defined as consuming at least 6 units (women) or 8 units (men) on a single occasion. Taking all adults who had had an alcoholic drink in the past year, 58% of men and 36% of women had drunk 6–8 units on at least one occasion; 71% of 16- to 24-year-olds had done so – 81% of young men and 60% of young women. Young adults, particularly males, were also the group most likely to have frequent heavy drinking sessions, although very few did so every day (Table 5).

Not surprisingly, young adults were also more likely than older people to have felt drunk during the past year; 77% of 16- to 24-year-old drinkers had felt drunk, compared with 44% of all adult drinkers. Young adults were also the group most likely to have set out on a drinking session with the intention of getting drunk and to have had frequent hangovers. Over half of the young adults (54%) who had been drunk at least once in the past year had started out with the intention of getting drunk on at least one occasion, compared with 30% of all adults (about one in eight of all drinkers). A similar proportion (55%) of 16- to 24-year-old drinkers said they had a hangover at least once a month.

Table 5 Frequency of heavy drinking (6 or more units on one occasion for women, 8 or more units for men) (%)

	16–24 yrs			All ages 16–75+		
	All	Males	Females	All	Males	Females
Drunk 6–8 units on one occasion in the last year? (%)						
Yes	71	81	60	47	58	36
No	29	19	40	53	42	64
How often do you drink this amount? (all those answering 'yes' to above, %)						
Almost every day	0	0	0	1	2	0
Several days a week	5	5	5	5	7	2
Once or twice a week	37	47	21	28	33	19
Once or twice a month	32	31	33	25	26	23
Less often	26	17	40	41	32	56

Source: Goddard (1998)

Round drinking is considered to be one factor that may encourage heavy sessional drinking (by drinking to keep up with the rest of the group). However, according to the above survey, young adults are no more likely than other adults to buy drink in rounds: 69% of 16- to 24-year-olds who had drunk alcohol in a pub or club in the last year had bought a round of drinks, compared with 67% of all adult drinkers and 78% of 25- to 44-year-olds. There were no gender differences among young adults with regard to round buying, in contrast to older age groups where men were much more likely than women to buy rounds. Moreover, respondents generally did not think that drinking in rounds encouraged people to drink more – 69% thought it made no difference (Goddard, 1998). More findings from this study on young people's attitudes to getting drunk are presented in Chapter 3 and their experience of harmful consequences is reviewed in Chapter 6.

A survey of drinking in Wales in 1993 also found that 'binge drinking' was most prevalent among young adults aged 18–24, especially young men. Binge drinking was defined as drinking half the adult weekly maximum recommended units of alcohol in one session, i.e. 7 units for women, 10–11 for men. Nearly a third of drinkers aged 18–24 reported binge drinking at least once a week, compared with a quarter of 25- to 34-year-olds and falling to 15% of the over-55s. Young people who were single and had not completed further education after leaving school were particularly likely to binge drink. While binge drinking correlated with consumption levels, it was not solely confined to heavier drinkers: 16% of adult males and 7% of females who drank within the weekly sensible drinking levels also reported binge drinking at least once a week (Moore, Smith and Catford, 1994).

Daily drinking

The switch in sensible drinking advice to daily benchmarks may be more relevant to young people's interest in binge drinking than the previous emphasis on weekly levels, but it may still not be perceived by young people as relevant to them, because most of them do not drink every day. Young adults do drink more alcohol than any other age group, but they are least likely to be daily drinkers (NTC, 1994; Prescott-Clarke and Primatesta, 1997; Goddard, 1998). The Health Survey for England, conducted in 1995, found that among the 16–24 age group, only 8% of young men and 4% of young women were daily drinkers. Proportions of daily drinkers rose steadily with age to 27% of men and 16% of women aged over 75. There is little correlation between how often people drink and the amount they consume. As they get older, adults are more likely to drink every day, even though they tend to drink less in total (Prescott-Clarke and Primatesta, 1997).

Are more or fewer young adults choosing not to drink?

Young adults are less likely than older people to be non-drinkers. In 1996, overall, 7% of men and 13% of women claim they never drink; these proportions are unchanged since 1984. However, among young adults aged 16–24, not only are there fewer non-drinkers, but there is also little difference between the sexes – in 1996, 8% of young men and 9% of women say they never drink (ONS, 1998). Over the whole time period of General Household Surveys, 1984–98, the proportion of young adults who claim not to drink has also remained fairly constant; however, there are fewer non-drinkers in 1996 (9%) than there were in 1994 (11%).

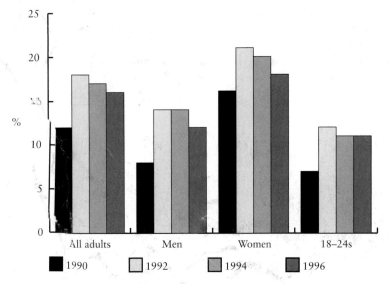

Source: NTC Publications (1994, 1997)

Figure 7 Teetotal trend. Proportion never drinking alcohol

According to market research surveys conducted for the drinks industry in the mid-1990s (NTC, 1994)* an increasing proportion of young adults report never drinking alcohol, in common with all adults. This claim takes 1980 as its base. If data from 1992, 1994 and 1996 are examined (Figure 7), then it would seem that the trend based on this data set is also levelling out or reversing. In the late 1990s, the proportion of non-drinkers among 18–24s may be reducing, although there are still more non-drinkers than there were in 1980. Data for more years are needed to ascertain the direction of any teetotal trend.

Student drinking

A recent, United Kingdom-wide survey of alcohol consumption by university students found that students are more likely to drink above recommended weekly limits than their peers in the general population (Webb *et al.*, 1996). The survey involved 3075 second-year students from ten United Kingdom universities. The sample reflected the inter-faculty,

---

* Caution should be exercised in interpreting data from drinks industry sources, as sampling and research methods are not published.

ethnicity and sex distribution at United Kingdom universities. Most (94%) of the sample were aged 18–25, with a median age of 20; 6% of the sample were mature students aged 26–65. Over half (54%) the male students in the sample drank more than 21 units per week, including 16% who drank more than 50 units per week. Forty-two per cent of female students drank over 14 units per week, including 9% who drank over 35 units per week. Male students averaged 32 units per week and females 17 units. Nearly one-third of male students and a quarter of females admitted binge drinking (defined as 11 units or more in one session for men and 7 units for women).

This is the first large-scale study of student drinking in the UK. Earlier smaller samples, in individual higher or further education institutions, found that students' alcohol consumption was broadly similar to that of young people of the same age in the general population (West, Drummond and Eames, 1990; Anderson, 1984; Collier and Beales, 1989).

Thus, young people's drinking patterns have changed and are continuing to change. Compared to 1980, in the 1990s young adults are drinking more, on fewer occasions. Nevertheless it should not be forgotten that the majority of young drinkers do not drink to excess and that consuming alcohol is normal behaviour across this age group.

Young people also alter their drinking habits as their circumstances change or they enter different life stages. For example, drinking patterns adopted as students are usually not sustained after leaving college, when typically the frequency and amount of drinking reduces. Marriage or a stable relationship are important moderating influences on young men's drinking habits, which reduce even further when they become parents (Power, 1992; Backett and Davison, 1992). There is some truth in the statement 'they'll grow out of it'!

Socio-economic and educational factors and young people's alcohol consumption

Many of the socio-demographic factors found to be associated with adults' drinking habits are not relevant to children. Among adult women and less clearly among men, those in non-manual households have higher average alcohol consumption than do those in manual households. Men in households headed by an employer/manager are more likely to exceed the former sensible weekly levels than those in other households. Levels of adult alcohol consumption are also positively associated with household income and for women, with individual earnings (Bennett *et al.*, 1996).

National survey data on family spending on alcohol in 1996–7 indicate that the poorest tenth of the population spent £3.35 per week and the richest tenth £25.53. These data do not separately identify spending by young people, although it does confirm the General Household Survey data, in finding that spending on alcohol varies by employment status. It is highest among those who are full-time employed and self-employed (£16.96 per week), and lowest among those who are unemployed, economically inactive and retired (£9.42 per week). There are also variations in spending by occupational grouping and by region. The heaviest spending on alcohol occurs among those who are employers or managers. The heaviest spending region is the North (ONS, 1997c).

The limited available data relating to children and teenagers are confusing. *Tomorrow's Young Adults* (HEA/MORI, 1992a) a national survey of 9- to 15-year-olds in England, found that consumption varied little between socio-economic groups, except that children of professional and managerial parents drank less. Until 1996, the ONS series of surveys of young teenagers' drinking did not attempt to gather socio-economic information based on parents' jobs as it was felt that children would have difficulty in providing accurate information. In the 1996 study of young teenagers in England and Scotland, indicators of socio-economic position were used: ownership of home, car, home computer and dishwasher (Goddard, 1997b). There was no consistent association between drinking behaviour and these indicators, although in contrast with the HEA/MORI survey and consistent with adult drinking patterns, the evidence does suggest that it is young teenagers from better-off families who are most likely to drink alcohol. Young teenagers from families with two or more cars and those whose homes had dishwashers were more likely to be frequent drinkers than other children. However, there was no association with computer or home ownership.

The above survey also examined young teenagers' educational expectations in relation to drinking. The picture is tentative and confusing, but suggests that 11- to 15-year-olds from better-off families and who have low educational expectations are the group most likely to be frequent drinkers. Forty-five per cent of frequent drinkers from families with two or more cars did not expect to stay on at school after taking GCSEs. Pupils who expected to sit GCSEs but not get good results were more likely to drink alcohol at least once a week than either those who expected good results or those who did not think they would be taking GCSEs. Those who did not expect to stay on in full-time education post-16 were more likely to drink frequently than those expecting to stay on; this was especially true of boys (Goddard, 1997a).

There is relatively little information available on social class differences in alcohol consumption within older teenagers and young adults. None of the regular monitoring surveys includes data on socio-economic status, partly because of difficulties in measurement across an age band which straddles the ages at which socio-economic status is defined by parental occupation/income or by own occupation/earnings.

Today's Young Adults the HEA national survey of 16- to 19-year-olds in England, found that at 16–18 regular drinkers were most likely to be male and from social class group AB. However, while this group were most likely to be drinkers, they were *least* likely to exceed the adult sensible drinking levels (HEA/MORI, 1992b). By their early 20s, it is individuals in the higher socio-economic groups who are more likely to be drinking at risky or unsafe levels (Alcohol Concern, 1997a).

The ESRC 16–19 research initiative (1986–1990) collected information about the development of 16- to 19-year-olds in relation to education, employment, leisure and political values. This study found that, as indicated by the data on adult drinking, finance was a very important factor in accounting for variations in alcohol consumption among this age group. Those who drank the most were those who had the most money to spend (Roberts, 1988).

The British Paediatric Society and Royal College of Physicians report, *Alcohol and the Young*, suggests that income and employment combine to influence young people's alcohol consumption:

'...young people who feel excluded from society because they are out of work or in boring, humdrum jobs are more likely to drink heavily than those studying or in interesting occupations; on the other hand, those with more money in their pockets are likely to be able to drink more.' (Royal College of Physicians, 1995, p. 34–5)

The contribution alcohol makes to inequalities in health, for young people of all ages in Britain, is not known. National studies comparable to that of Makela, Valkonen and Martelin (1997), on the contribution of deaths related to alcohol misuse to socio-economic variation in mortality in Finland, have not been replicated in the UK. In Finland, the role of alcohol in socio-economic differentials was greatest in the younger age groups of adults (aged 20–50). Alcohol's contribution to inequalities was modest in deaths from diseases, but substantial in accidental and violent deaths. One-half of the difference between Finnish manual workers and upper non-manual workers (aged 20 and above) in accidental and violent mortality could be attributed to alcohol-related deaths. The authors emphasise that these findings are not generalisable to other countries and postulate that alcohol use is likely to make a smaller contribution to inequalities in mortality in Britain because of the relatively small and irregular social class differences in mortality from liver cirrhosis and relatively low mortality from liver cirrhosis, accidents and violence. However, there is ample justification for this type of analysis to be done on British mortality statistics, because *Our Healthier Nation* (Department of Health, 1998) acknowledges that accidents and violence are major causes of death among young people and alcohol is a major contributory factor.

SETTINGS FOR DRINKING: WHERE DO YOUNG PEOPLE DRINK?

Generally, young people are introduced to alcohol by their parents in the home, go on to drinking with friends in other places at around 13–14 years of age and begin to drink alcohol in pubs from the age of about 14–15 upwards.

By far the most common setting in which young teenagers in England, Scotland and Wales usually drink alcohol is at home, with parents (HEA/MORI,1992b; Marsh, Dobbs and White, 1986; Turtle, Jones and

Hickman, 1997; Balding, 1997; Goddard, 1997a). In Northern Ireland, a national study in 1989 found that young drinkers were not introduced to alcohol by their parents, but had their first drink in a public place and with friends (DHSS Northern Ireland, 1989). Comparing young teenagers drinking in Northern Ireland and Scotland, Loretto (1994) found that 11- to 16-year-olds in Northern Ireland were more likely than their Scottish peers to drink alcohol in peer groups in uncontrolled settings. However, recent HBSC data for Northern Ireland in 1992 and 1994 suggest that settings for drinking alcohol are not so different from the rest of the UK. Parents are by far the most common source of alcohol for 11- to 12-year-olds and between one-quarter and one-third of the sample drank alcohol at family gatherings (HPANI, 1994, 1995).

A common stereotypical image is of young people drinking furtively at friends' homes, in parks or on street corners. The HEA survey of 9- to 15-year-olds in England conducted in 1989 (HEA/MORI, 1992b) found that in reality only a very small proportion (4%) *regularly* drank in any of these settings. A higher proportion had ever drunk in these settings (29% in friends' houses and 15% in park/street), and the proportion rose with age: 54% of 15-year-olds have ever drunk alcohol at friends' houses and 37% have ever drunk in parks/street.

The more recent HBSC survey in England, conducted in 1995, using a differently framed question, confirmed that the most common drinking situations for 11- to 15-year-olds were 'with parents' (69%) and 'with friends' (52%). Importantly, this survey found that the more young people drank, the less likely they were to drink with parents and the more likely to drink with friends (from 22% of those drinking 'hardly at all' to 88% of those drinking 'quite a lot' or 'heavily'). It was also the heavier drinkers who said they usually drank when feeling down or troubled or when alone (44%) and this group were much more likely to drink during school breaks (9%) or on the way to and from school (6%). This analysis did not control for age, although the age trends showed a similar pattern, with 14% of drinkers in year 11 (15–16) saying that they drank when feeling down or troubled (compared to 10% of year 7) and 12% drank alone (7% in year 7).

The ONS survey of young teenagers' drinking in 1996 found that there were marked differences between young teenagers in England and

Scotland, in terms of where they usually drank and who they usually drank with (Goddard, 1997a, 1997b). In England, 11- to 15-year-olds were much more likely to say they usually drank at home or someone else's home (52%) compared to their peers in Scotland (41%). The Scottish sample were also less likely to say they usually drank at parties and pubs or clubs and more likely to say that they drank somewhere else – probably outdoors (46% in Scotland, 26% in England).

As might be expected, drinking with parents at home reduces as teenagers get older and they have more opportunities to drink elsewhere and with friends. At around age 13, young people begin to drink alcohol occasionally at parties, clubs or discos, with a third of 15-year-olds occasionally drinking in these settings.

Drinking and buying alcohol in licensed premises

All surveys have found that pub or bar drinking is rare under 13, but rises with age. Survey results vary in the proportions of young teenagers who say they drink in pubs, depending on how the question is phrased. By 15, one-half of young people in England claim to have had a drink in a pub (HEA/MORI, 1992b). In 1996, nearly a quarter of 15-year-olds in England and rather less in Scotland said they *usually* drank in a bar or pub (Goddard, 1997).

Lister-Sharp (1994) noted these and other methodological difficulties in estimating the prevalence of 'under-age' drinking in licensed premises in a review of the research since 1970. She concluded that there is no evidence that the extent of 'under-age' drinking has increased or decreased in the past 20 years. The proportions of under-18s drinking in licensed premises increases with age, as they find it easier to pass for 18. Under-age drinking appears to be more prevalent in England than in the rest of the United Kingdom.

Throughout the United Kingdom, young teenage girls, especially 15-year-olds, are more likely than boys to drink alcohol in discos or clubs. In England, 11- to 15-year-old girls are also more likely than boys to drink in bars and pubs, while in Northern Ireland, this pattern is reversed.

Buying alcohol

Most under-18s who buy alcohol appear to be able to purchase it easily, both in licensed premises and off-licences (Marsh, Dobbs and White, 1986). Even young teenagers seem to be able to buy alcohol fairly easily – a quarter of 11- to 15-year-old drinkers in England, Scotland and Northern Ireland have bought alcohol from off-licences (Goddard, 1997a, 1997b, HPANI 1994). When they start to buy alcohol, younger adolescents use off-licences, shops and supermarkets. Purchasing alcohol from supermarkets is more common among young teenagers in Scotland than in England (21% compared with 13%). This is likely to be a reflection of different patterns of alcohol outlets in the two countries. Purchasing on licensed premises becomes the norm among 17-year-olds.

The University of Exeter's HRBQ data for 1996 from a large, but non-random sample of secondary-school children, includes information about purchase of alcohol in the last seven days (Balding, 1997). Figure 8 shows the purchasing patterns of years 8–10 (12–15) in 1996. Buying alcohol increases with age, although it should be noted that the majority of respondents, even in year 10 did *not* purchase alcohol from any of the outlets listed in the last seven days. The off-licence was the most widely used outlet for both boys and girls; about 1 in 6 respondents in year 10 (including non-drinkers), claimed to have bought alcohol from this source. This represents two-thirds of the 14- to 15-year-olds who said they had purchased alcohol in the last seven days. In contrast, supermarkets had the lowest level of patronage; Balding suggests that 'policing' of their drinks shelves and checkouts has a deterrent effect. Comparing year 10 purchasing patterns for 1996 with those recorded ten years earlier for the 1986 data set, Balding notes that in 1996 fewer purchases were being made from a pub or bar and more from an off-licence.

Marsh, Dobbs and White (1986) asked how young people in England usually obtained alcohol in licensed premises. About half of the 13- to 14-year-olds in their sample said their relatives bought it for them, but by age 15 most said they bought it for themselves. In a study of 10- to 14-year-

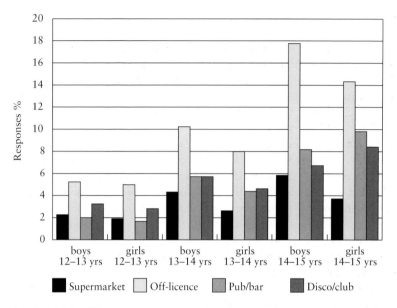

Adapted from Balding, 1997

Figure 8 Have you bought alcoholic drink at any of these places during the last 7 days?

olds in Scotland by Aitken (1978) 85% of those reporting drinking on licensed premises said a parent had been present and 75% said a parent, usually their father, had given them a drink.

Less than half young people say they have been refused service because of their age and this has been the experience of fewer girls than boys, perhaps because girls look physically mature earlier than boys (Lister-Sharp, 1994). One North American study (McCall, 1997) found that the more physically attractive a young woman is perceived to be by a bartender, the less likely she is to be asked for proof of age when purchasing alcohol.

The HEA survey of 16- to 19-year-olds in England (HEA/MORI, 1992a) found that for this age group, pubs and wine bars were the preferred venue for regular drinkers. Almost 90% had ever consumed alcohol in pubs or wine bars and nearly half regularly drank in pubs. Only 6% said they regularly drank at parties and 17% regularly drank at home. Thus drinking at home does not cease, but the shift to drinking in licensed premises marks the transition to adult status and social relationships, as noted by Dorn (1983) in his ethnographic study of young people who were leaving school and taking up employment. This trend towards pubs, clubs and wine bars as the preferred setting for drinking continues within the young adult age group 18–24.

Social contexts

Drinking alcohol is a sociable activity. Following their introduction to drinking alcohol within the family, adolescents incorporate alcohol into their own social lives with their friends. A study by Bennet, Smith and Nugent (1989) of 15- to 24-year-olds in Wales found that this age group were less likely than any other age group to drink alone and more likely to drink in a mixed-sex group.

A series of ethnographic studies of city centre pub drinking in the North East of England, Gofton (1990), has confirmed the important part that drinking alcohol plays in young people's leisure pursuits. Young people of both sexes drink mainly at weekends. In the North East of England, Friday nights are for single-sex groups and Saturday is couples night. Groups of young people gather together at the outskirts of town at the beginning of the night and move systematically around a circuit of pubs and clubs in the town centre, visiting 8 or 9 venues in one evening. Sex and courtship are very important for both sexes. The main reason for going to the pubs is to see and be seen by other young people, so personal style and image are considered to be very important. The types of drinks consumed are chosen to be part of the fashionable image.

BEVERAGE PREFERENCES: WHAT DO YOUNG PEOPLE CHOOSE TO DRINK?

Young people drink more than one kind of alcoholic drink. Among under-16s, girls are more likely than boys to consume a variety of drinks (Goddard, 1997a, 1997b). Until the 1990s, novice drinking by young people was characterised by the occasional drink of relatively weak beverages such as shandy, with parents, at home. They moved on to drinking beer, lager, cider and wine as they reached mid-teens. Very few under-16s drank spirits. Diversification of the drinks market during the last decade has provided drinkers, including young people, with a wider choice of alcoholic beverages. This has been reflected in changes in the types of drinks consumed by young people so that beverage preferences in the 1990s are markedly different to those observed for young people in the 1970s and 1980s.

Brain and Parker (1997) point out that the drinks industry needed to diversify and the youth market, being the heaviest drinkers, was an important target:

> 'with beer sales down by 35% in less than 20 years and the transfer to home drinking, particularly of imported wines, the reconstruction and revitalisation of the youth drinks market is a crucial strand in the industry's attempts to keep up its market share.'   (p. 10)

The drinks industry also faces stiff competition from others for the young people's spending power:

> 'One young adult's decision to buy a designer jacket or a pair of trainers instead of going out drinking for two or three weekends is more threatening to the alcohol industry than any decision to switch the place of drinking or what is drunk. A young person's willingness to purchase cannabis for home use, or a soft drink at a night club to supplement one night of Ecstasy is just as crucial and damaging to sales.'   (p. 11)

In order to appeal to the youth market, the drinks industry introduced a proliferation of bottled lagers and ciders, flavoured wines, aperitifs and cocktails – collectively dubbed 'designer drinks'. These are packaged and marketed to appeal to the under-30 age group and more importantly from a health promotion perspective, they are characterised by a high alcoholic strength (% ABV). For example Mad Dog 20/20 (13% ABV) is a fortified wine; Diamond White (8% ABV) is a strong white cider. In summer 1995, another product range hit the shelves in the UK, with the introduction of alcoholic soft drinks such as lemonades and colas. Within a year over 100 new products had been produced (Whitbread, 1997). Alcopops, as they soon became known, are characterised by their sweet taste and high % ABV and rapidly became popular. Market analysis by the drinks trade suggests that by the millennium, alcopops will double their volume sales to 200 million litres, with a retail value of £750 million (*The Grocer*, 1997, cited in Roberts *et al.*, 1997).

Concern about the appeal of these new products to children and 'under-age' drinkers has prompted a flurry of research activity to find out whether their availability is encouraging more young people to start drinking, or to drink at an earlier age, or to drink in more risky ways.

Alcohol Concern, politicians and other agencies have accused the alcohol industry of exploiting children's beverage preferences in marketing alcopops. The HEA surveys of schoolchildren in England conducted in 1989 and in 1995 found that the overwhelming majority of children up to the age of 12 prefer soft drinks to alcoholic beverages of any kind (HEA/MORI, 1992b; Turtle, Jones and Hickman, 1997). Preference for soft drinks declines with age, as novice drinkers develop a taste for alcohol, but by age 15, 60% still prefer soft drinks (Turtle, Jones and Hickman, 1997). While enjoyment increases with age, very young adolescents generally do not enjoy the taste of alcoholic drinks. Consequently, it is argued, alcopops will particularly appeal to youthful palates because they taste like soft drinks. Comparing beverage preferences of young teenagers in England in 1989 and 1995, the two HEA studies indicate an increase in the proportion of 11- to 15-year-olds who say they enjoy the taste of alcohol, at all ages from 11–15. In 1995, three-quarters of 15-year-olds said they enjoyed the taste. The 1989 survey found that those who get more drinking practice soon develop a taste for alcohol, with two-thirds of regular drinkers in the 9–15 age group claiming to enjoy the taste of alcohol. Children from social class AB household are significantly more likely to claim to enjoy the taste than those from social class DE (HEA/MORI, 1992b).

Recently published studies commissioned in response to concern about designer drinks and alcopops provide a fairly comprehensive picture of what young people, especially under-18s, are drinking in the 1990s. One of the first studies to draw attention to the impact of the first wave of designer drinks was a longitudinal study of 14- to 16-year-olds in the North West of England (Newcombe, Measham and Parker, 1995) which suggested that young people's beverage preferences, even among these novice drinkers, are particularly susceptible to fashion and style influences. Half of the North West sample reported drinking bottled strong lager, while a quarter to a third of drinkers consumed 'Snakebite' (lager and cider) or designer labels such as white cider (for example Diamond White) or fortified wines (for example Thunderbird).

Questions about the new drinks are now beginning to be incorporated into continuing monitoring surveys – to date the ONS survey of young teenagers in 1996 (Goddard, 1997a, 1997b), and the 1996 Welsh HBSC monitoring survey (Roberts *et al.*, 1997). There are also several recent cross-sectional studies: two national studies in England (Raw and McNeill, 1997; Balding, 1997); one national study in Scotland (Crawford and Allsop, 1996); plus several local/regional studies in Scotland (for example McKeganey *et al.*, 1996; Forsyth, Barnard and McKeganey, 1997; Hughes *et al.*, 1997) some of which have combined surveys with qualitative methods such as observation and focus groups (Hughes *et al.*, 1997). Only the results relating to consumption patterns will be discussed here. Data relating to young people's attitudes and knowledge about different beverages will be discussed in subsequent sections.

Alcopops and designer drinks have undoubtedly rapidly become established as part of young people's drinking repertoire in the 1990s, particularly among the under-18s. However, the new drinks have not necessarily replaced the more traditional drinks; beer, lager and cider remain the most popular drinks consumed, even by young teenagers. The 1996 ONS survey of 11- to 16-year-olds in England and Scotland found that alcopops were most commonly drunk by those who had consumed four or more different types of alcoholic drinks in the past week, i.e. those who already had a varied drinking repertoire. Very few young people drank only alcopops (Goddard, 1997a). Alcopops drinkers were also more likely to drink shandy, fortified wines and spirits, all drinks where the taste of alcohol can be masked with mixers. This provides some support for the suggestion that young people drink alcopops because they can't taste the alcohol.

In England and Scotland, recent national and local studies conducted during 1995–6 have found that after beer, lager and cider, alcopops are the next most commonly consumed drink among under-16s, followed by spirits (Raw and McNeill, 1997; Hughes *et al.*, 1997; Goddard, 1997a, 1997b). Several studies in Scotland and England have established that the peak age for drinking alcopops is 13-16, well below the legal age limit for alcohol purchase (Hughes *et al.*, 1997; Raw and McNeill, 1997; McNeill *et al.*, in preparation). Furthermore, alcopops' popularity and market share declines with age (Goddard, 1997a) whereas the popularity of other drinks increases with age.

Cider is particularly popular with 15- to 16-year-old girls (Raw and McNeill, 1997) and in Scotland, a 1996 survey of 15- to 17-year-olds in four Scottish cities found that the majority of respondents said their first alcoholic drink was cider (Crawford and Allsop, 1996). Wine is not a popular drink with young teenagers. Sex differences in alcoholic beverage preferences are apparent even in novice drinkers aged under 16. While beer is the most commonly consumed drink for both sexes, girls are more likely to favour wine and sherry/Martini (HEA/MORI, 1992b). In Wales in 1996, 17% of 11- to 16-year-olds reported consuming alcopops at least weekly and here, these drinks were more popular than any other drinks apart from beer and lager. As reported above (see 'How many young people drink and how much do they drink?'), trends in other beverage consumption in Wales over the decade 1986–96 showed little or no change in weekly consumption of beer, cider, wine or spirits for 11- to 16-year-olds as a whole, but significant age and gender differences. Weekly beer and cider consumption by 15- to 16-year-olds significantly increased for both sexes – beer from 39% to 54% in boys and from 19% to 27% in girls. Weekly cider consumption decreased significantly across the decade for 11- to 12-year-olds; from 18% to 8% in boys and from 8% to 3% in girls.

Whether the new designer drinks and alcopops encourage more young people to start drinking, or young drinkers to drink more, rather than simply influence the brand preferences of existing drinkers is not yet established. This would require longitudinal and case-control data that are not yet available. The increase in frequency of drinking and amounts consumed by young teenage drinkers pre-dates alcopops, but roughly parallels the main diversification of the drinks market. The Welsh HBSC monitoring study (Roberts *et al.*, 1997) found that for boys and girls in the youngest (11–12) age group, the increase in weekly drinking from 1994 to 1996 exactly matched the proportion drinking alcopops and no other alcoholic drink (alcopops were introduced in summer 1995). The authors consider that drinking of alcopops accounts for half of the increase among 13- to 14-year-olds and for most of that among 15- to 16-year-old girls. This argument may be attractive, but as a hypothesis, further work is required to determine whether this association is a *causal* relationship. The 1996 ONS study found no evidence to support the contention that alcopops encourage young people to start drinking.

Two Scottish studies have established that beverage choice is related to drunkenness among schoolchildren. Consumption of some of the new designer drinks, particularly the white ciders (for example Ice Dragon, TNT, White Lightning) and fruit wines (for example Thunderbird, Mad Dog 20/20, Ravers) are significantly related to drunkenness (Forsyth, Barnard and McKeganey, 1997; McKeganey *et al.*, 1996) and high unit consumption on the last drinking occasion (McKeganey *et al.*, 1996). Forsyth, Barnard and McKeganey (1997) also found that consumers of vodka were significantly more likely to have been drunk on their last drinking occasion. They usually obtained these drinks from shops or via friends. However, alcopops drinkers were no more likely to have been drunk than the average drinker and tended to obtain these drinks from family members or friends. Drinkers who obtained their alcohol of any type from family members were less likely to have been drunk.

Self-presentation and image are especially important to young people, so alcoholic drinks are chosen to present a particular message to the peer group (Newcombe, Measham and Parker, 1995) and the drinks industry has been quick to exploit this in packaging and marketing new drinks products. The evidence from studies of young people's views on designer drinks and alcopops is consistent with the view that these drinks are indeed very appealing to young people (McNeill *et al.*, in preparation; Hughes *et al.*, 1997; Brain and Parker, 1997). This has even been admitted by the drinks industry (Whitbread, 1996; Gould, 1997). By the mid-teens, young people are developing a sophisticated awareness of brand image. For young teenagers with limited spending power, this will be coupled with value for money assessments to select products which will give 'more bangs per buck' (Coffield and Gofton, 1994), i.e. the greatest level of intoxication for the cheapest price. Strong beers and lagers, ciders, 75 cl bottles of fruit wines and vodka have high % ABV and therefore represent value for money, particularly if shared between a group of young drinkers.

Moreover, it seems that many teenagers and young adults consciously use alcohol as a mood-altering drug and both seek and expect to get drunk (Newcombe, Measham and Parker, 1995; Gofton, 1990). This is reflected in the range of drinks consumed by 16- to 24-year-olds and the manner in which it is consumed. At the moment, the market for ordinary strength beer is declining. The major drink for young people is strong lager, particularly cans/bottles of foreign lager. Young people also invent their own cocktails (much to the horror of older drinkers) such as 'Snakebite' or 'Blastaway' which are highly potent and fashionable. Newcombe, Measham and Parker (1995) suggest that young women in particular find the strong 'confectionery' products appealing, for example Malibu, Tequila Sunrise, Taboo, Thunderbird.

As described earlier, binge drinking is particularly prevalent among young people because intoxication is deliberately sought (Gofton, 1990; Bennett, Smith and Nugent, 1989; Moore, Smith and Catford, 1994; Newcombe, Measham and Parker, 1995; Goddard, 1998). In the qualitative studies of city centre drinking in the North East, young people were observed to adopt drinking styles which achieved the best 'buzz', in the same way as users of illegal drugs. Many said they drank for 'strong effect' and that they would choose a drink because of its potency (Gofton, 1990). The moderation message is therefore unlikely to appeal to young people.

Statistics on alcohol sales (NTC, 1997) confirm these qualitative data. Young men are the group most likely to drink lager: 18- to 24-year-old men were responsible for 25% of all lager consumed in 1996. Of all male adult beer drinkers, the 18–24 age group drink the most beer per week , but they now drink less than in 1980. Total weekly beer consumption in all male adults in 1980 averaged 12 pints (24 units) in 1980 and 10 pints (20 units) in 1996. For 18- to 24-year-old male beer drinkers, average consumption was 15 pints/week (30 units) in 1980 and 12.9 pints/week (25 units) in 1996.

Low alcohol beers are unpopular with young people and increasingly so, especially with young men. The age group 18–24 accounted for just 18% of total consumption of low/no alcohol beers and lagers in 1988 and only 14% in 1992.

It has already been noted that cider is a popular drink with young people, especially young women, although they are increasingly switching to the new white ciders, which tend to be much stronger than the traditional types. In 1993, the age group 18–24 accounted for 33% of all cider consumed; by 1996, this age group accounted for only a quarter of cider consumption. Women accounted for half of all cider consumed in 1996.

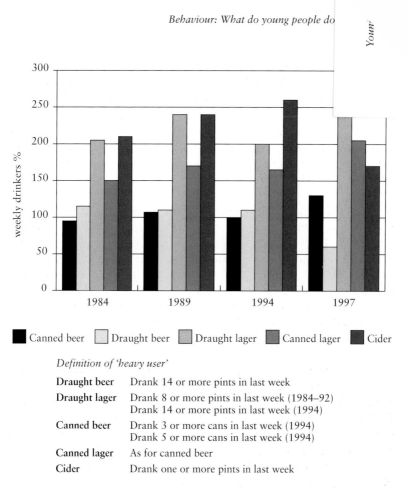

Definition of 'heavy user'

Draught beer	Drank 14 or more pints in last week
Draught lager	Drank 8 or more pints in last week (1984–92) Drank 14 or more pints in last week (1994)
Canned beer	Drank 3 or more cans in last week (1994) Drank 5 or more cans in last week (1994)
Canned lager	As for canned beer
Cider	Drank one or more pints in last week

Source: NTC Publications (1994).
Note: As indicated above, some definitions of a heavy user are different for the periods 1984–92 and 1994 and therefore comparisons between these different time periods should not be made.

Figure 9 Heavy users index of intensity of beverage usage among 18- to 24-year-olds

There has been a steady growth in the amount of 'designer' packaged cider (bottles/cans) consumed by this age group since 1988, from 28% to 31% in 1996. Of 18–24s who have drunk cider in the last week, average consumption is 4 pints a week; 18–24s also have a high heavy user index for cider, beer and lager, as shown in Figure 9.

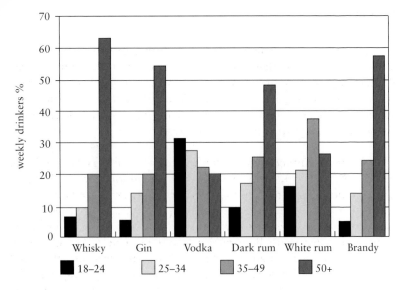

Source: NTC Publications (1994)

Figure 10 Profile of weekly spirits drinkers

Young adults are less likely to drink wine than older people, although in 1996 they did account for 22% of the wine consumed. They show a preference for white or rose wine. Young adults are also not heavy users of the traditional fortified wines (port, sherry or vermouth) but are the main consumers of the designer cocktails referred to earlier. They also show a marked preference for white rum and vodka spirits, having a high weekly consumption and heavy user index for each of these drinks, but consume less of other spirits and consume them infrequently compared to other age groups (Figure 10 and Table 6).

Table 6 Heavy user index, for vodka and white rum, 18–24 age group

	1983	1988	1993	1997
Vodka	176	217	193	243
White rum	162	111	138	122

(Definition of heavy user: Drank one or more measures in last week)
Source: NTC Publications (1994)

ETHNICITY

In addition to the significant gender differences already described, ethnicity, culture and religion are all important factors in young people's alcohol use, but very little research has been done in Britain on these issues. Most of the national studies from which the prevalence and consumption figures given above are derived, do not differentiate young people by ethnic group or religious affiliation.

An Addictions Forum/Aquarius conference, Alcohol Services for Black People, held in 1994, highlighted the lack of information available on cultural differences in relation to alcohol use. For example, relatively little is known about South Asian people and alcohol, and even less about South Asian young people's drinking. The few studies on South Asian ethnic groups that have been published (for example Cochrane, 1989) have tended to focus on adult problem drinkers and their use of alcohol treatment services. These studies reveal that problem drinking exists for certain South Asian males at levels comparable to the white population and that alcohol services tend not to be sensitive to their needs.

All three main religious denominations of the South Asian communities in the UK, Hinduism, Islam and Sikhism, prohibit the use of alcohol (Ghosh, 1984). However, as with other religious groups, doctrine and actual behaviour do not always match. Ghosh points out that alcohol has been used in the Indian sub-continent for many years by a variety of religious, cultural and socio-economic groups. Taking a historical perspective, he concludes that no cultural tradition, (even among Muslims) is against the use of alcohol in any form and under any circumstances. Cochrane (1989) found that a minority of all three religious groups in the UK used alcohol. He describes a continuum of acceptance of alcohol from Sikhs (more socially acceptable) through Hindus to Muslims (less socially acceptable). Among all Asian cultural groups, it is considered less socially acceptable for women to drink than for men.

The subjective impressions of Asian alcohol fieldworkers (Ahmed, 1988; Asad, 1994) are that today's young Asians are drinking more than previous generations. Few studies have examined ethnic differences in young people's alcohol consumption, let alone trends, or even taken such issues into account when considering the accuracy of their data.

Denscombe (1995) points out that, apart from not acknowledging the needs of different ethnic groups, studies which do not take account of ethnic and religious differences may considerably underestimate the extent of alcohol use among white young people.

At a national level the only available data are from three HEA studies, one a qualitative study (Mathrani, 1998) and two national surveys of the health behaviour of school-age children in England, conducted in 1989 (HEA/MORI, 1992b) and 1995 (Turtle, Jones and Hickman, 1997). The 1995 survey forms the first year of the continuing HBSC monitoring survey and will provide much needed data on drinking trends among different ethnic groups of schoolchildren. The two surveys used different age groups (9–15 in 1989, 11–16 in 1995), sampling methods and questions and so are not directly comparable. However the two data sets offer indications that drinking patterns among young non-white teenagers may be changing alongside those of their white peers. Both surveys found that Black and Asian young people continue to have less experience of alcohol than white pupils of the same age.

The 1995 HEA survey included a separate sample alongside the main sample to represent the ethnic communities resident in England. Just over half of the ethnic schools sample had tasted alcohol – 72% of black pupils and 27% of Asians. These proportions are similar to those of the 1989 survey, allowing for age differences. However, for Black and Asian pupils who drank, the amount drunk was similar to that of white pupils, although a higher proportion said they hardly drank at all (41% compared to 34% of the main sample) and correspondingly less drank a 'moderate amount' (16% compared with 22%). Black and Asian pupils drank all types of alcohol less often than their white peers did and black teenagers drank less frequently than Asian drinkers. These patterns differ from those noted in 1989, when black 9- to 15-year-olds were more likely to have tried alcohol than either white or Asian pupils and to drink as frequently as white teenagers.

Given the likelihood of parental disapproval, it is not surprising that the 1995 survey found that both Black and Asian drinkers are less likely to drink with their parents than white pupils. However, in contrast, the small number of African-Caribbeans who participated in the HEA's qualitative research (see below) described their drinking as being within the moderating context of family life, at family gatherings and, as older teenagers, at the pub with parents. The HEA surveys found that both black and Asian young drinkers are more likely than white teenagers to drink on their own and that Asian drinkers are far more likely to drink when feeling down.

The 1989 HEA survey found that Irish and Southern European children had particularly high weekly consumption rates compared to other ethnic groups.

The HEA's qualitative study involved focus groups and interviews with friendship pairs of young *drinkers* aged 13–20 in 13 English towns (Mathrani, 1998). The sample included young African-Caribbean and South Asian drinkers. The numbers involved were small and the fact that they were all drinkers means that the results are unlikely to reflect the experience and views of the majority of young people from these ethnic groups who are non-drinkers. The young Hindu women drinkers, saw drinking alcohol as an adventurous act of rebellion against the norm of prohibition. Their drinking started later than their white peers, at 14–15, took place secretly in the company of relatives, consuming strong drinks quickly because of fear of being discovered. Drinking is not associated with socialising with peers. For the older girls, the freedom of leaving home for college can lead to temporary episodes of extreme drunkenness before establishing moderate drinking habits.

Young male Hindu drinkers reported that their culture allowed them to drink. At around age 15, some had been introduced to alcohol by their fathers, while others drank covertly with their peers in the same way as white and African-Caribbean boys. Drinking moderated in late teens due to work and exams. Young Hindu men who drink are not opposed to their younger female family members drinking, suggesting a change in attitude to drinking by Hindu girls in future.

This study found that Muslim young people 'officially' describe themselves as non-drinkers, although those recruited into the study did drink from 14–15 onwards. This finding suggests that responses by Muslim young people in 'official' surveys about drinking behaviour may not necessarily be accurate. Both Hindu and Muslim drinkers receive minimal parental guidance on alcohol and there is no sensible drinking model. Both Hindu and Muslim boys talked of drinking to forget about family and school worries and the high expectations placed on them by their families. Because they are allowed to go out unaccompanied, Muslim boys have more opportunity than girls do to drink alcohol. Those girls who do drink, do so with boyfriends rather than other young women.

A local survey of alcohol consumption among 15- to 16-year-olds in Leicestershire (Denscombe, 1995), also found a much lower frequency of drinking alcohol among South Asians, across all religious groups, compared to white young people. The vast majority of the South Asians (94%) described themselves as non-drinkers, while only 2% said they drank alcohol two or more times a week. In contrast, only 38% of the white 15- to 16-year-olds said they were non-drinkers and a quarter drank alcohol twice a week or more.

2. Knowledge: What do young people know about alcohol?

SUMMARY

1. Young people know about the harmful effects of alcohol and their knowledge develops as they mature.

2. In common with adults, young people's awareness of units and sensible weekly levels is quite high, but the ability to relate these concepts to their own drinking behaviour is less common.

3. Sensible weekly drinking levels have little relevance to young people's chosen pattern of 'binge drinking'. The focus on daily benchmarks in the current sensible drinking guidelines is more relevant to young people's drinking styles. Compared to other adult age groups, young adults (aged 16–24) are less likely to have heard anything about the changes in the sensible drinking levels but also most likely to be interested in them. Young women are the least likely group to have heard about the changes.

4. Young people consider alcohol to be less harmful than other drugs, including illegal substances, caffeine, tobacco and solvents.

5. Young people from minority ethnic groups are less knowledgeable about alcohol.

6. The research data on young people's knowledge about alcohol are based on information considered by researchers as important for young people to know. We know little about the way young people themselves define, prioritise, organise or interpret information about alcohol, in order to make sense of their social worlds.

*

Young people's knowledge about alcohol has received scant attention in the research literature, in comparison to the measurement of behaviour, attitudes, values, beliefs and expectancies. On first consideration, this is surprising, given that development of young people's knowledge about alcohol is a mandatory component of the English National Science Curriculum for schools, at all key stages from ages 7–16 (Department for Education, 1995). The knowledge required under the national curriculum is essentially concerned with the harmful effects of alcohol and particularly the effects on health and body functions. Knowledge of units and sensible drinking levels is not required.

The lack of research interest may derive from the overwhelming concern about young people's drinking *behaviour*. Nevertheless, accurate and up-to-date knowledge is acknowledged as a component in health behaviour models and it can be argued that young people have a right to know the physiological, pharmacological and biological facts about alcohol. Indeed, access to accurate and relevant information is one of the few felt needs expressed by young people themselves in relation to alcohol education, at least within informal settings (Young, 1990).

Limitations of the data

Some of the large-scale surveys of adolescent drinking have included questions about knowledge, but detailed responses are not presented in the published reports unless they are significantly related to drinking behaviour or socio-demographic factors (Hawker, 1978; Plant *et al.*, 1990). Similar comments apply to the few British evaluation studies of alcohol education with young people, which record pre- and post-intervention knowledge levels (Bagnall, 1991; Baldwin, 1990).

Studies of early conceptual and cognitive development relating to alcohol among children provide more in-depth information than the studies of teenagers and young adults. Studies of the latter groups usually involve fairly crude knowledge tests, often a list of statements requiring yes/no or agree/disagree responses. Such data provide little information about young people's overall understanding of alcohol 'facts' or how they organise their concepts about alcohol within broader cognitive structures. The way statements are phrased in some studies could allow a respondent to give a high percentage of 'correct' answers whilst failing to see the relevance of alcohol facts to her/his own drinking behaviour. For example, Black and Weare (1989) asked young people to give yes/no answers to a series of statements prefaced by 'If a person regularly drinks too much it can cause...'. Respondents who did not think that they regularly drank too much might therefore correctly identify the harmful effects of alcohol without thinking that these facts applied to them.

To increase knowledge is a common objective for local and national alcohol education programmes but, unfortunately, published accounts of local interventions are rare. Some of the information presented here derives from unpublished data that were collected by the HEA to inform, monitor and evaluate their Drinkwise campaign 1989–94. It is mainly quantitative data collected by market research organisations using a range of sampling methods to identify the alcohol-related knowledge, attitudes, awareness and behaviour of adults (16+) in England during the period 1989–94 (BMRB, 1994).

CHILDREN AND YOUNG PEOPLE AGED 10–16

Young people enter their teens with considerable knowledge about alcohol. Children begin to acquire this knowledge from an early age, long before they start to drink, or even taste, alcohol themselves. Young children can identify alcoholic drinks by smell and/or photographs and can recognise drunkenness. Awareness of the concept of alcohol and understanding of adult motives for drinking have also been demonstrated in children as young as 5 years of age (Jahoda and Crammond, 1972; Gaines *et al.*, 1988; Fossey, 1992).

Two local studies of 12- to 13-year-olds (Bagnall, 1991; Boyns, 1993) have found that at this age, young people are fairly clear about the harmful physical effects of alcohol, the legal age for buying alcohol and can identify alcoholic beverages (although in Boyns' study, 20% thought that ginger-beer contained alcohol). Both studies report confusion about unit equivalents and alcoholic strengths of drinks, especially cider, with a tendency to overestimate the equivalent strengths of spirit measures compared to long drinks. Bagnall found that 60% of 12- to 13-year-olds wrongly estimated that a single whisky was stronger than a pint of beer.

This confusion about strengths of alcoholic drinks continues in 14- to 16-year-olds. The English national sample of 14- to 16-year-olds (Plant *et al.*, 1990) found that 56% of boys and 52% of girls wrongly reported that a single whisky was stronger than a pint of beer, 26% of boys and 28% of girls thought all beers contained roughly the same amount of alcohol. Also 25% of boys and 21% of girls wrongly estimated that a glass of wine contains much more alcohol than a glass of cider. The male heavy drinkers in this sample were significantly more likely to wrongly estimate the single whisky/pint of beer equivalents, with 70% of male heavy drinkers answering incorrectly. In contrast, female heavy drinkers were significantly more knowledgeable about these equivalents than other females, and were also more likely to know that eating slows down the effects of alcohol.

Two recent qualitative studies confirm that young teenagers in the 1990s continue to be uncertain about the strengths of alcoholic drinks. A youth panel consultation exercise with 10- to 17-year-olds was conducted for the Portman group in 1996–7. Responses to a true/false quiz indicated that panellists were better informed about the law and basic facts than they were about beverage strengths. Age differences were not identified. Girls were slightly more knowledgeable than boys. Two-thirds of panellists believed coffee can sober you up and there was little awareness of the health benefits to adults of moderate drinking (Fox, 1997). Interviews with friendship pairs and focus groups of 140 young people aged 13–20 conducted for the HEA in 1995 identified very low awareness of the units system, especially among younger participants. They tended to think in terms of glasses or cans and there was a tendency to underestimate how much alcohol was considered safe (Mathrani, 1998).

This confusion about units and equivalents is hardly surprising, given that at this age, most young people are novice drinkers, occasionally consuming small quantities of alcohol. The new designer drinks and alcopops are sold in a variety of volumes and containers, with a range of % ABVs requiring a calculator to work out the unit equivalent. Young teenagers' drinks will often be home/self-poured, into non-standard glasses, or from a bottle or can, often shared with friends, rather than standard pub measures. Until young people gain some experience of consuming alcohol in standard pub measures, it is difficult to explain the concept of unit equivalents. The HEA has recognised this in its recent alcohol literature for young people, which gives examples which are more relevant to their beverage preferences than the 'one unit = a half-pint of beer or a small glass of wine' message. Grasping the concept of units may be particularly difficult for young people whose experience in school is of volume measured in metric measures, in contrast to the imperial measures used in licensed premises. Additionally, their experience at home will be of adults' home-poured measures, which for spirits and wines are known to be considerably more generous than standard measures (Robinson, 1989). Therefore their apparently inaccurate knowledge may simply reflect an accurate account of their own experience of drinking an ever-widening range of drinks in non-standard measures, or of observing others doing the same.

It is also worth noting that although they have more experience of drinking standard measures, adults are also often confused about unit equivalents (HEA/MORI, 1992a).

YOUNG PEOPLE AGED OVER 16

Rather more information is available about young adults' knowledge about alcohol, from surveys commissioned by HEA for their Drinkwise campaign, the HEA's national monitoring survey of adult health in England in 1996 (ONS, 1997d) and a limited number of local studies.

Monitoring data from the HEA Drinkwise campaign (BMRB, 1994) and the more recent ONS survey, reveal higher levels of knowledge in 16- to 24-year-olds compared to all adults aged 16–54. Young adults are rather more knowledgeable than other adults in relation to awareness of units (88% in 1996 compared with 80% of all adults) and estimation of the unit content of various drinks (Hansbro *et al.*, 1997). Data collected for Drinkwise found that 16–24s were also more aware of the existence of recommended weekly limits for men and women (72%) and the 'alcohol by volume' labelling method (74% compared to 59% of all adults) (HEA, 1990).

While general awareness of units and limits is higher among young adults, only a minority can correctly estimate the number of units in specific drinks (HEA/MORI, 1992a; ONS, 1997d). Even after being told the number of units in beer, most 16- to 19-year-olds do not know how many units there are in other drinks. In general, in common with younger teenagers and adults, they tend to overestimate the number of units in other drinks relative to beer's unit content (HEA/MORI, 1992a).

In 1996, 46% of 16- to 24-year-olds correctly identified the number of units in a pint of beer and a glass of wine and 36% the units in a single pub measure of spirits. Respondents in social classes I and II and heavier drinkers were more likely to give the correct units in each drink. These estimations of units in drinks have been adopted by the HEA as intermediate indicators to monitor progress (Hansbro *et al.*, 1997).

Prior to the switch from weekly to daily sensible drinking levels, conflicting results were obtained for young people's knowledge of 'safe' or 'recommended' drinking limits, which may derive from the way questions were framed in different studies. Young adults' awareness of the changes in sensible drinking levels from weekly to daily benchmarks were explored in an HEA survey of adult health in England in 1996 (Hansbro *et al.*, 1997). The 16–24 age group were more likely than older respondents to say they had not heard anything about the changes (38% compared to 26% of all adults) but least likely to say they were not interested in them (28% compared to 38% of all adults). Young women were the least likely group to have heard about the changes in sensible drinking levels (46% of 16- to 24-year-old women). However, those 16- to 24-year-olds who had heard about the changes were no more likely to be confused about them (13%) than were adults in general. Differences by social class and levels of consumption are not further broken down by age. For all adults, the respondents in social classes I and II, and heavy drinkers of both sexes were the least likely to feel confused about the changes, while the respondents in social classes IV and V were most likely not to have heard about them. Non-drinkers and those drinking less than one unit per week were much more likely than others to say the changes were of no interest to them.

Though it predates the current daily benchmarks, the survey of 17- to 18-year-olds in Southampton by Black and Weare (1989) is relevant because it asked about daily drinking. Young people were asked how much beer or wine a person would have to drink *each day* to suffer from an illness caused by alcohol. Respondents significantly *overestimated* the 'safe' levels (*judged by the researchers as 8 units/day for men and 5 for women!*) and were particularly likely to overestimate their definition of a 'safe' level for beer consumption. They were aware that the risky levels were lower for women, and 17- to 18-year-olds in work, rather than further/higher education or training, and those whose parents were in manual occupations, were significantly more likely to overestimate 'safe' limits.

The 1994 HEA Drinkwise campaign evaluation (BMRB, 1994) found that young adults aged 16–24 were as knowledgeable as all adults (aged 16-55) in estimating the *'recommended weekly limits'* for men and women. Only 12% of 16- to 24-year-olds (compared with 11% of all adults) correctly knew the recommended limits for both sexes, 16% of 16–24s knew the recommended male level (21 units), compared with 15% of all adults and 20% knew the recommended female limit (14 units), compared with 16% of all adults. More young adults also overestimated the female limit with 27% of 16–24s estimating more than 14 units, compared to 17% of all adults.

An HEA survey (HEA/MORI, 1992a) of 16- to 19-year-olds asked young people to estimate *in units*, the *safe weekly limits*. The majority response to a question framed in this way was to set a weekly limit in terms of units that is *lower* than the recommended sensible drinking level of 14 units per week for women and 21 units for men. However, in common with the Southampton survey, a substantial minority of young people set higher than recommended limits for lager and beer (the preferred drink for this age group). Over half of 16- to 19-year-olds who exceeded the sensible drinking level in the previous week thought the male limit for beer or lager was higher than 21 units.

This evidence is consistent with the binge drinking patterns adopted by young people. As mentioned in Chapter 1, many young people concentrate their drinking into a small number of heavy drinking occasions rather than spread their consumption evenly throughout the week. It may be that while young adults were aware of the message about sensible drinking levels in terms of weekly units, they were unclear about sensible levels for one drinking occasion. They could therefore judge themselves to be drinking safely in consuming more than 8 units (if male) or 5 units (if female) on one occasion, while not exceeding a total of 21 or

14 units in the week. Acknowledgement that weekly consumption levels can have little relation to single drinking episodes and may mask binge drinking was one of the factors which led to the change in focus of the sensible drinking guidelines from weekly levels to daily benchmarks (Department of Health, 1995).

The Southampton survey found that, as reported for younger teenagers, 16- to 18-year-olds have a good knowledge of the most publicised harmful effects of alcohol on physical health such as liver damage and high blood pressure and of the risks attached to drinking in pregnancy. However, the way some of the questions were phrased would allow respondents to answer correctly, without acknowledging their personal relevance. Their general knowledge about alcohol was found to be limited – less than one in five knew that the relative price of alcohol has declined in the last 20 years and less than half knew that more people die from alcohol than from illegal drugs (Black and Weare, 1989).

The latter finding may accord with more recent data on young people's views on how harmful alcohol is in relation to other drugs. The HBSC survey (Turtle, Jones and Hickman, 1997) asked young people in year 11 (15- to 16-year-olds) how harmful they thought different drugs were. Alcohol was evaluated as the least harmful of all the drugs listed, less harmful than caffeine, cigarettes, glue sniffing or any illegal drugs. This comparative ranking applied to all ethnic groups, and both genders, although Black and Asian young people were twice as likely to say alcohol was 'very harmful' than their white peers. As noted earlier, this apparent contradiction between young people's high levels of knowledge about alcohol-related harm and their low assessment of its harm related to other drugs may reflect lack of sophistication in measurement tools or a real cognitive inconsistency. These findings suggest that comparative assessment of the risks attached to use of different drugs, including alcohol, should be a priority for alcohol education programmes.

A survey of health educators and sixth-formers concluded that the latter group are generally well informed and show higher knowledge levels about alcohol than certain groups of health educators, for example nurses (Kemm and Rowe, 1992). However, despite its mandatory inclusion in the science national curriculum, and the fact that alcohol education will appear in some guise within every secondary-school curriculum, not all young people are aware of having experienced alcohol education at school. Recent HEA surveys found that only two-thirds of 15- to 19-year-olds recalled having received any alcohol education while at school (HEA/MORI, 1992a, 1992b). Younger adolescents and those who drink least were the most likely to agree that 'young people do not know enough about the dangers of drinking', while older teenagers and regular and heavier drinkers were least likely to agree with this statement. This finding might be expected, as people tend to respond in ways that justify or defend their behaviour.

MINORITY ETHNIC GROUPS

A small-scale survey conducted by the HEA (1994) to inform their Drinkwise campaign found that young adult drinkers from Hindu, Muslim, Sikh, African and Caribbean minority ethnic groups were less knowledgeable about alcohol than white young people. They knew less about the terminology used in alcohol education (sensible drinking, units, and limits) but were better informed than older people from those ethnic groups. Very few 16- to 24-year-olds could correctly define a unit, although the majority were familiar with the term %ABV. Only a third were aware of the 'Sensible Drinking' concept and this term was felt to be inappropriate and offensive by Muslims. Over half had heard of weekly adult sensible drinking levels, but hardly any 16- to 24-year-olds could correctly define them.

Relevant knowledge?

The research data on young people's knowledge about alcohol is based on information considered by researchers as important for young people to know. We know little about the way young people themselves define, prioritise, organise or interpret information about alcohol, in order to make sense of their social worlds.

3. Attitudes: What do your people think about alcohol

SUMMARY

1. From an initially neutral stance, young children up to the age of about 10 years develop increasingly negative attitudes to alcohol and to drinkers. They hold stereotypical beliefs about gender roles and are aware of adult motives for drinking.

2. After the age of 10, attitudes to alcohol become more positive in parallel with increased personal experience of drinking. Young drinkers aged 9–15 perceive the social benefits of drinking. The transition from negative to positive attitudes within the 11–13 age group has received little research attention.

3. Among 11- to 16-year-olds, heavier drinkers are more likely to hold positive attitudes to alcohol and to value the social benefits. They are more likely than others to say that they drink to relax, to socialise, for curiosity, to relieve boredom and because all their friends drink. Heavier-drinking boys are also more likely to think it is safe to drive after one or two pints.

4. Schoolchildren who drink alcohol are more likely than non-drinkers to express negative attitudes to school and to teachers.

5. Fifteen- to sixteen-year-olds consider alcohol to be less harmful than any other drug, including cigarettes and caffeine.

6. As young people enter their mid- to late-teens and become more experienced drinkers, so their attitudes change and develop. Most young people, including light/moderate drinkers say they drink for positive reasons. In contrast with younger teenagers, heavier drinking females are significantly more likely to drink to boost their self-

confidence. As with younger teenagers, heavier drinkers of both sexes are more likely to say that they drink alcohol 'to get drunk'.

7. From the age of 16, young people hold similar attitudes to alcohol to those held by the general adult population.

8. There is some evidence that, while alcohol comes relatively low on scales of personal concern, it is of greater concern to young people than to adults. Young people's concerns are about the possible negative consequences of drinking, rather than with drinking *per se.* Young adults may evaluate binge drinking as life enhancing rather than life threatening.

9. Most young adults describe themselves as moderate or light drinkers and only a small minority worry about their drinking.

10. The expectancies associated with drinking alcohol are: appearing adult, disinhibition, reducing tension, enhancing sexuality, enhancing social interaction, increasing assertiveness and facilitating aggression.

11. Young people, especially heavier drinkers, admit to drinking 'to get drunk' and, compared to adults, are more tolerant of drunkenness. They consciously plan to 'binge drink' on certain occasions and perceive that their friends approve of this practice. Young people do not consider the more serious consequences of binge drinking to be likely outcomes; while they believe they have the skills to control their drinking, they may not apply them in binge drinking situations.

12. We currently have little information about social norms for drunken behaviour among young people. Nor do we know much about the self-control strategies that young people adopt. Further research in this area would be useful.

13. Young people are more vigorously anti-drink driving than adults. However, those young people who hold the least emphatic views are those who claim to have driven while intoxicated. In comparison to older adults, young people aged 16–24 are less likely to be able to judge their personal safe limits for driving and more likely to claim to be able to drive without their ability being affected. More British

research is needed into young people's attitudes, assessment of risk and behaviour in relation to riding as a passenger with someone who has been drinking.

14. Young people have positive attitudes to the new alcoholic beverages – designer drinks and alcopops. These drinks are particularly appealing to the mid-teen age group. Young people choose alcoholic beverages that are consistent with their attitudes to drinking and their alcohol expectancies.

15. The 15–24 age group, in common with all other ages, think that pubs should have 'atmosphere', and that good ventilation, alcoholic drinks, comfortable seating, soft drinks and decor are important. Atmosphere and music are particularly important to young people.

16. Young people have rather less interest than older people in stricter controls on alcohol sales, advertising or taxation. They share the strong general public support for unit labelling of cans and bottles of alcoholic beverages and for compulsory training courses for publicans and licensees. They also hold rather less strong views than adults do on moral issues.

17. The ethnic group to which young people belong has been largely ignored in attitude studies. More research is needed into the place and meaning of alcohol among young people from minority ethnic groups.

*

CHILDREN AND YOUNG TEENAGERS

From an initially neutral stance, young children up to the age of about 10 years develop increasingly negative attitudes to alcohol and to drinkers. Children, especially girls, tend to judge female drinkers more harshly than male drinkers, suggesting that young children's cognitive structures incorporate traditionally learned gender differences (Jahoda and Crammond, 1972; Spiegler, 1983; Fossey, 1992, 1994).

Young children's attitudes toward alcohol have changed little in the past twenty years. Comparing Jahoda and Crammond's findings from 1972 with her study conducted in 1992, Fossey found only two significant differences: children in the 1990s were slightly less negative towards male drinkers, and female drinkers were judged more harshly by girls than boys.

By the age of 8, most children hold stereotypical beliefs about gender roles and have negative attitudes towards alcohol. They have an awareness of adult motives for drinking (Gaines *et al.*, 1988) and begin to acquire more positive expectancies regarding alcohol. These increase as they begin to experiment with alcohol. After the age of 10, attitudes to alcohol become more positive and children enter adolescence with cognitive structures which are already positively oriented towards drinking (Davies and Stacey, 1972; Aitken, 1978).

In contrast with the carefully researched findings available on early development of alcohol attitudes in the pre-teen age group, the transition from negative to positive attitudes within the 11–13 age group has received little recent research attention. Some inferences can be drawn from large-scale quantitative studies that include this stage of development within a broader age band.

A small-scale qualitative study conducted in the South West of England (Hanmer-Lloyd, 1989) with 11- to 13-year-olds found that by this age, children exhibit positive beliefs about the effects of alcohol while having little real experience of these effects. There is a conflict between children's overall attitude that drinking is a 'good thing to do' whilst also believing it to be foolish. They generally see alcohol as being bad for health, for example the liver, but are not aware of how alcohol actually affects the body. Their favourable attitudes relate to viewing the drinking of alcohol as an essential way to gain adult status.

Large-scale studies of schoolchildren conducted over the last twenty-five years have all found that young teenagers develop increasingly favourable attitudes to alcohol as they get older. Not surprisingly, their attitudes are consistent with their behaviour; the more they drink, the more favourable their attitudes are to drinking alcohol (Davies and Stacey, 1972; Aitken, 1978; HEA/MORI, 1992b; Turtle, Jones and Hickman, 1997).

Identification of time trends in attitudes to alcohol among schoolchildren is difficult, for the reasons discussed earlier, most particularly comparison between studies using different samples and methods and questions. Attitudes are also not usually the main focus of the large-scale studies, the main interest being in describing young people's drinking behaviour. Aitken's study in 1978, of the development of attitudes and drinking behaviour of 11- to 14-year-olds in Scotland, remains one of the most detailed large-scale studies of early development of alcohol-related attitudes. However, given the recent changes in schoolchildren's drinking behaviour and the correlation between positive attitudes and alcohol consumption, Aitken's conclusions may not apply to young people in the 1990s.

It would be particularly interesting to know whether the gender differences in peer approval of drinking observed by Aitken continue to apply. In 1978, boys were found to be less severe in their judgement of drinking by other boys, than the girls were about drinking by other girls. The majority of both sexes made the same judgements about the opposite sex as they did for their own sex. However, those who did make different judgements tended to use a double standard – girls drinking was judged more severely than boys.

More recent studies have tended to record relatively few significant gender differences in attitudes among young teenagers. Where differences have been observed they are less marked than those related to alcohol consumption and are in the direction of boys holding more favourable attitudes to the social benefits of alcohol than girls of the same age. Boys are more likely than girls to drink alcohol to give them social confidence (HEA/MORI, 1992b; Turtle, Jones and Hickman, 1997; Plant, Bagnall and Foster, 1990).

In the light of the trends towards increased alcohol consumption, it would also be interesting to know whether young teenagers in the 1990s continue to hold the negative attitudes to both non-drinkers and heavy drinkers that were observed in the 1970s. Both Davies and Stacey (1972) and Aitken (1978) found that young adolescents see both non-drinkers and heavy drinkers as less sociable and less attractive than their 'ideal self': heavy drinkers because they are seen as rowdy and extroverted, non-drinkers because they are introverted. Aitken also found that as children move into their teens, their 'ideal self' image becomes more extroverted, so the drinker's image becomes more attractive while the non-drinkers image becomes less attractive. In contrast to 11- to 14-year-olds in general, the behaviour of male heavy drinkers of that age matches their 'ideal self' image as rowdy extroverts and their positive attitudes to other boys who are heavy drinkers.

Aitken's study considered young people's attitudes to alcohol in relation to their self-image and their social relationships with their peers. Since the 1970s, attitude studies have continued to confirm that young people identify the social benefits of drinking at an early stage in their drinking careers (Davies and Stacey, 1972; Aitken, 1978; Plant, Peck and Samuel, 1985; Plant, Bagnall and Foster, 1990; HEA/MORI, 1992b; Turtle, Jones and Hickman, 1997).

The HEA's HBSC survey found that among 11- to 15-year-olds in England, the proportions agreeing that drinking alcohol increases self-confidence, makes life more fun and helps in making friends, increase dramatically with age (Table 7).

Table 7 11- to 15-year-olds' attitudes to statements by school year (n = 6406)

	Year 7 (11–12 yrs)	Year 9 (13–14 yrs)	Year 11 (15–16 yrs)
Those agreeing:			
Life is more fun when you have a drink	13	25	43
I feel more confident when I have a drink	8	22	54
It is easier to make friends when you have a drink	7	14	32

Source: Turtle, Jones and Hickman (1997), p. 115

The same survey examined schoolchildren's drinking in relation to their attitudes to school and their expectations of what they would be doing once they reached 16. Young people who drank alcohol were more likely than non-drinkers to express negative attitudes to school and to teachers. There were particularly divergent views on fair treatment: drinkers were less likely than non-drinkers to agree that school rules are fair (46%

compared to 66%) and that their teachers treated them fairly (56% compared to 71%). Young drinkers were also more likely than non-drinkers to feel pressurised by school work and to feel parents and teachers expected too much of them. This was particularly apparent in years 7 and 9. In contrast, their own expectations of academic study after 16 were lower than those of non-drinkers (Turtle, Jones and Hickman, 1997).

YOUNG HEAVIER DRINKERS

In the 11–16 age group, descriptive studies have found that the more young people drink, the more likely they are to hold positive attitudes to alcohol and to particularly value the social benefits attached to drinking (Davies and Stacey, 1972; Aitken, 1978; Plant, Peck and Samuel, 1985; Plant, Bagnall and Foster, 1990; HEA/MORI, 1992b; Turtle, Jones and Hickman, 1997). A national survey of 14- to 16-year-olds in England found that heavier drinkers are more likely than others to say they drink to relax, to socialise, for curiosity, to relieve boredom and because all their friends drink. Heavier drinking boys are also more likely to think it is safe to drive after one or two pints (Plant, Bagnall and Foster, 1990). Similar findings are reported by Sharp and Lowe (1989) and Turtle, Jones and Hickman (1997).

Qualitative research commissioned by the HEA found that among schoolchildren, heavier drinkers saw drinking alcohol as an escape from problems and stress, particularly family worries and examinations (Mathrani, 1998).

OLDER TEENAGERS AND YOUNG ADULTS

As young people enter their mid- to late-teens and become more experienced drinkers, so their attitudes change and develop. Foxcroft and Lowe (1993) explored the reasons given for drinking by 16- to 19-year-old YTS trainees in Humberside. They confirmed that most young people drink for positive reasons – because they like the taste, relaxation, celebration and socialising. Unlike the findings for younger teenagers, they did not find that heavier drinkers were more likely to drink for recreation – this was a reason given by the majority, regardless of level of alcohol use. In complete contrast to the pattern for younger teenagers, it was heavier drinking *females*, and not males, who were significantly more likely to drink to boost their self-confidence. As with younger teenagers, heavier drinkers of both sexes are more likely to say that they drink alcohol 'to get drunk'. Also, the heavier the drinker, the more reasons they give for drinking.

From the age of 16, young people hold broadly adult attitudes to alcohol. The HEA market research survey for Drinkwise (NOP, 1990) indicates that they share adults' views on the legal age for drinking (it should not be lowered); on further controls on the price and sale of alcohol (disapprove) and generally have the same views on alcohol and health.

THE SALIENCE OF ALCOHOL ISSUES TO YOUNG PEOPLE

In comparison to other long-term health influences, young people share adults' views that drinking has less influence on health than smoking, practising safer sex or stress, and about the same importance as exercise and diet. The survey also found that 16- to 17-year-olds, women of all ages and socio-economic groups AB appreciate greater alcohol-related health risks at all levels of alcohol consumption. Most young adults describe themselves as moderate or light drinkers and only a small minority worry about their drinking. Three-quarters of 16- to 19-year-olds do not feel their drinking is harmful to their health. Heavier and more frequent drinkers are more likely to personalise the health risk but it is still only a minority who worry about how much they drink. Alcohol also comes relatively low on scales of personal and general concern, being of lesser concern than AIDS, heroin abuse, tobacco smoking, street violence, the effects of pollution or poisons in food. However, while the general pattern of concerns is the same for all ages, young people are more concerned than adults about AIDS and about alcohol (NOP, 1990).

Table 8 Concern about the effects of alcohol by age group

Concern about the effects of alcohol:	Total	16–17	18–24	25–34	35–54	55+
– to the nation (%)	29	45	33	27	29	26
– personal (%)	12	18	12	12	13	9

Source: NOP Market Research, 1990

A qualitative study also confirms that young people do see alcohol as an important health concern. In Durham, an action research project into young people's perceptions of health needs (Lewthwaite, 1990) involved consultations with 265 young people aged 14–25, individually and in groups. For both sexes, alcohol-related health needs were in the top five priorities. Alcohol came fifth for young women, after (in order) appearance, mental health, pregnancy, contraception/abortion and sex. Young men's concerns were (in order) appearance, sex, alcohol, mental health and smoking. The young people expressed strong positive reasons for drinking. Their concerns were not about drinking *per se* but about the possible negative moral and social consequences, for example whether they would be caught drinking by the police or their parents (also noted by Fox, 1997, in youth panel group meetings), or not being able to remember what they had done when they had been drunk. Young men were also concerned about the social consequences of excessive drinking, although they defined excessive at levels far higher than 'official' levels. Neither sex was concerned about addiction to alcohol.

Two qualitative studies in Edinburgh and South Wales offer an interesting interpretation of the meaning and salience of alcohol as a health issue for young people (Backett and Davison, 1992). The general aim of both studies was to investigate the meaning of health and illness within particular socio-cultural settings – the domestic group and the local community. The authors point out that health education has traditionally tried to explain the irrationality exhibited by people who indulge in harmful or risky health behaviours (such as binge drinking) in terms of defective culture (ignorance, fatalism) or defective individuals (fecklessness or acquiescence). They suggest (p. 56) that a more plausible explanation is to distinguish between what is rational and what is reasonable:

'Rationality is (in theory) free of cultural impediments. What is rational behaviour to an Italian is also rational behaviour to an Eskimo. Reasonable behaviour acknowledges that knowledge, belief and perception about the workings of the universe (including health) may vary between and within cultural groups.'

They suggest that health behaviours such as drinking should be assessed in terms of the images of acceptability and appropriateness for different population groups. They present evidence that suggests that the social construction of 'reasonable' health behaviour is a basic principle of social life. Their respondents' assessments of what is reasonable health behaviour were based on three sets of ideas:

- age, physiological function and risk

- cultural norms of responsibility in social relationships

- financial and temporal constraints consequent on demographic position (for example student).

Life-threatening risky behaviours, for example binge drinking, were considered acceptable for young unattached people, but inappropriate for the family person. Young, single adults were viewed as having bodies that could deal with toxins, such as alcohol, so enjoyable though potentially threatening behaviours such as binge drinking were viewed as *life enhancing* by most respondents and something to be tolerated, especially as they would probably not last. Younger respondents tended to claim that it was 'boring' or 'middle aged' to worry about lifestyle implications for illness. Their expressed concerns, about having a 'fit', 'healthy' or 'slim' body were usually related to sexual attractiveness or peer acceptability rather than preventive medicine. When young adults became parents, they claimed to have become more aware of their own health and no longer took health for granted. Child care took up time and money that had previously been available for personal pursuits, including going to pubs, clubs and parties. Excessive alcohol consumption was considered too costly and disruptive to family obligations.

EXPECTANCIES

Psychologists have established that drinkers' expectations of what will happen to them when they drink are very important determinants of their actual behaviour. Placebo experiments have shown that merely *believing* that they have had a drink of alcohol, regardless of actual alcohol content, leads people to act in ways that they would normally expect to behave when under the influence of alcohol (Marlatt and Rohsenau, 1980).

A novice drinker experiences certain effects which, together with observations of what happens to parents and peers when they drink, are then translated into expectations (expectancies). People hold both positive and negative alcohol expectancies (McMahon, Jones and O'Donnell, 1994). The positive expectancies (Brown *et al.*, 1980) associated with drinking alcohol are:

• appearing adult

• disinhibition

• reducing tension

• enhancing sexuality

• enhancing social interaction

• increasing assertiveness.

Negative expectancies include (McMahon *et al.*, 1994):

• impaired thinking, speaking and co-ordination

• facilitates aggression

• feeling ill the day after.

If young people expect to enjoy themselves more if they drink, they do have more fun. Similarly, if young people expect alcohol to cause less nervousness or enhance sexual experience, they are more likely to drink, and to drink larger amounts during sexual encounters (Leigh, 1990). Young men who expect alcohol to disinhibit them sexually are more likely to hold negative attitudes to condom use and less likely to use condoms (Gordon, Carey and Carey, 1997). Once an expectancy is confirmed by experience, and is valued by the young drinker, a behaviour pattern begins to be established, which will be reinforced in turn by the behaviour of the young drinker's companions.

Expectancies also vary with the amount of alcohol consumed. Recent research in the Netherlands (Wiers *et al.*, 1997) found that positive and negative expectancies predicted current drinking levels across three groups: 11- to 15-year-old schoolchildren, 16- to 18-year-old schoolchildren and first-year university students. Further longitudinal studies are needed to explore this area, which has important implications for prevention. For example, the authors found that 16- to 18-year-old boys had strong positive expectancies for high doses of alcohol and suggest that such expectancies could be challenged, as part of a preventive strategy.

ATTITUDES TO DRUNKENNESS AND 'BINGE DRINKING'

An important feature of young people's drinking is the meanings attached to drunkenness and binge drinking. The lack of uniformity over definitions of heavy drinking and binge drinking, in terms of amount/frequency, have already been noted as a factor which limits comparison of research reports. Adult researchers usually frame these definitions; they appear to have very different meanings to young people themselves.

For example, young adults may be heaviest drinkers in the population, but they do not see themselves as such. The majority describe themselves as moderate or light drinkers with only a small minority of young men (11%) and even fewer young women (4%) aged 18–24 actually classifying themselves as heavy drinkers. Only a small minority of young people worry about their drinking (HEA/MORI, 1992a). Similarly, the HEA's qualitative study of young drinkers found that young people do not see their drinking behaviour as binge drinking. They consider themselves to be drinking socially within their friendship group, even when the amount consumed in the session exceeds most researchers' definitions of binge drinking (Mathrani, 1998).

Young people, especially heavier drinkers, drink to get drunk. Recent qualitative studies have all reached similar conclusions about the centrality of intoxication in young people's drinking styles (Lewthwaite, 1990; Gofton, 1990; Gillespie *et al.*, 1991; Brain and Parker, 1977; Fox, 1997; Mathrani, 1998). After focus groups and interviews with friendship pairs of 140 young people in 13 towns in England, HEA researchers concluded:

> 'Young people drink *in order to* reach an altered state of mind and the idea of having one or two 'social' drinks is an alien concept. The youngest experimenters (13–15s) in particular were seeking a personal "buzz" or a "hit", a heady, drug-like sensation. This was also true of heavy drinking 16–20 year olds, especially males.'   (Mathrani, 1998)

Brain and Parker (1997) make similar observations following in-depth interviews with 55 12- to 17-year-old street drinkers in North West England, for most of whom getting drunk or getting a buzz was their primary reason for drinking. Moving on to older teenagers and young adults who drink in pubs and clubs, studies of some groups have found intoxication to be less important than for younger teenagers (Mathrani, 1998) while Gofton's (1990) study of young city centre drinkers in the North East of England found that in this context, young drinkers deliberately seek intoxication and tolerate drunkenness among their peers.

Lending support to the above conclusions about the importance of intoxication to young people, it appears that binge drinking is common to young people in other parts of the developed world, for example The Netherlands, North America, Australia and New Zealand (Harford and Grant, 1987; Gillespie *et al.*, 1991; Knibbe, Oostveen and Van de Goor, 1991). Gofton and Coffield's research in the North East of England (Gofton, 1990; Coffield and Gofton, 1994) and work in Australia (Gillespie *et al.*, 1991) have found that young people deliberately plan to binge on certain occasions, for example birthdays, end-of-term parties and New Year's Eve, and in the case of city centre drinkers, on Friday and Saturday nights. They perceive that their friends approve of and participate in binge drinking.

In the Queensland study (Gillespie *et al.*, 1991), of 16- to 18-year-old senior high school pupils, 71% of males and 67% of females had planned ahead at least once in the past 6 months, to make it a special occasion and drink a lot more than they usually did. A quarter of males and 16%

females planned to binge on 4 or more occasions in the past 6 months. They perceived drinking positively, anticipating that they would mix more easily and have more fun. While they acknowledged that hangovers and behaving stupidly were likely outcomes, they did not consider the more serious consequences, such as trouble with the police or fights, to be likely outcomes of binge drinking. This study also found that while practically all students believed that they had control over their drinking and could resist if they wanted to, the likelihood of their actually using alternatives to avoid drinking was not great. This is hardly surprising given that the purpose, from the student's perspective, was to get drunk. The most acceptable excuse was to say 'I'm driving'. Females were significantly more likely than males to use other alternatives to avoid drinking, such as non-alcoholic drinks, saying they'd 'had enough', leaving the situation or involving themselves in other activities.

There is also ample evidence from large-scale surveys that young people are more tolerant of drunkenness. National market research surveys conducted for the HEA in 1986 and 1990 found that young people are less likely than older people to agree that 'it is stupid to get drunk' or 'it is often unpleasant to be with someone who is drunk' (Wood, 1986; NOP, 1990). More recently, a national ONS survey of adults over 16 in England (Goddard, 1998) confirmed that young people view drunkenness in a much more positive light than older people. This survey found that young adults (16–24) are more likely than other age groups to identify drunkenness with feeling light-headed and relaxed, as well as feeling sick or having a hangover. They are less likely than older adults to mention slurred speech, being out of control or being argumentative. Compared to other ages, 16–24s who get drunk are twice as likely to do this deliberately and are more likely to agree that 'getting drunk is a part of the English way of life' and 'it is more socially acceptable to get drunk than to take illegal drugs'. Three-quarters of 16- to 24-year-olds who drink in pubs or clubs say that it does not bother them to be with a friend who is drunk. They are less likely than other age groups to agree that 'people shouldn't be served alcohol if they seem to be drunk' and that 'it is socially less acceptable for women to get drunk'.

Adults' moral disapproval of young people's drinking, and particularly drunkenness, may well have deterred researchers from asking research questions about this behaviour which will usefully inform health promotion interventions. For example, until very recently, the social norms for drunken behaviour among young people had received relatively little research attention. Qualitative studies in England (Mathrani, 1998; Gofton, 1990; Brain and Parker, 1997), Scotland (Dean, 1990) and in Australia (Burns, 1980; Gillespie, 1991) suggest that far from being chaotic, no-holds-barred behaviour, getting drunk is governed by social rules within the peer group. Ethnographic research in Australia among young men found that they will deliberately seek out social settings that permit certain behaviours. So 'getting rowdy with the boys' takes place in certain pubs known to condone heavy drinking, while the same young men will act much more moderately after the same amount of alcohol, at home or in mixed-sex groups (Burns, 1980).

The actual rules will be group and context specific, and it is therefore important that the findings from the qualitative studies of groups of young people are not generalised to *all* young people. For example, the HEA's qualitative study (Mathrani, 1998), while confirming that the amount young people consider is acceptable to drink varies with each drinking occasion, also noted pressure to conform to the mood of the particular group involved in drinking. In this way, even violence or aggression could be acceptable within the norms of a particular drinking group. While drinking in moderation was observed to have little appeal, there were also occasions where this was considered appropriate – a mid-week session between binges, for a more meaningful conversation than usual, or when a hangover might affect sport or a Saturday job. Non-drinkers were seen to be a small minority who rejected the core values of the drinking group.

The HEA study also identified important gender differences in standards of acceptable drinking behaviour. Girls saw sharing the same mood or level of drunkenness as most important, but not all having to drink the same amount to achieve this shared state. Boys, particularly pub drinkers, felt that it was inherently wrong to refuse a drink. Boys felt that actively seeking fights after drinking is unacceptable, although it commonly happens. Girls talked of intervening if a friend wanted to do something she might later regret. Both sexes disapproved of daily drinking, even in small amounts. Daily drinking, drinking at home or alone were seen by young people as signs of alcohol dependence. In the eyes of young people therefore, a large proportion of *adults* are seen as problem drinkers. The only acceptable excuse for not drinking, also noted in the study of 16- to 18-year-olds in Queensland by Gillespie *et al.* (1991), is being the nominated driver for the night. Even those too young to drive saw this as the only reason not to drink.

Further work is urgently needed to identify the social norms for drunken behaviour, moderate drinking and abstinence among different groups of young people in the UK. This should include exploration of the kinds of drunken behaviour, and levels of intoxication that are expected, tolerated or meet with disapproval by different groups. We also do not know much about the self-control strategies that young people adopt. Further research in this area would be useful.

ATTITUDES TO DRINKING AND DRIVING

Young people have strong negative views on drink driving and are more vigorously anti-drink driving than adults (NOP, 1990). A survey of 16- to 18-year-olds in Southampton found that the vast majority supported tougher measures to control drink driving. Most also thought it was fear of being caught rather than fear of an accident which prevents people from drinking and driving (Black and Weare, 1989). As stated in the previous section, young people consider driving to be an important reason for not drinking. A market research survey conducted by the Portman Group (1993) of a thousand, 18- to 30-year-olds found that 70% said they would abstain completely from drinking when they planned to drive home and 66% would make sure that someone in the group did not drink and drove the others home. Virtually all said that they would try to prevent someone they are with from driving if they thought they were over the limit. Favoured ways to stop someone from driving were confiscating car keys, talking them out of it and calling a taxi for them. In the 1995–6 West Midlands Young People's lifestyle survey, 90% of 11- to 16-year-olds agreed that people should never drink and drive (Sherrat, MacArthur and Cheng, 1997). A survey of year 8 (12–13) and year 10 (14–15) schoolchildren in ten local education authorities in England also found that most schoolchildren express the intention never to drink and drive, with proportions increasing with age (Balding *et al.*, 1997). However, one in five year 8 boys and one in seven year 8 girls do not agree that they will never drink and drive, reducing to one in six boys and one in ten girls by year 10. Half of this group think it is likely that they will be involved in an accident whilst driving.

Young people share adults' views on policy issues related to drinking and driving. Panel group discussions with young people commissioned by the Portman Group found that the vast majority agreed that 'people who drink and drive should be severely punished' (Fox, 1997). A 1994 survey conducted for the HEA (MORI, 1994) found that in common with public opinion in general, most 15- to 24-year-olds want the police to be able to conduct random breath tests on drivers; 85% agree with this proposal, 53% strongly agree. However, young people also share the general public's equivocal opinions on reducing the legal limit for alcohol in the blood when driving. Half agree with this proposal, but less than a third strongly agree and a third disagree. Those who drink frequently (more than three times a week) are least likely to support this measure and 40% disagree.

Worryingly, those young people who hold the least emphatic views on drink drive policy are those who claim to have driven while intoxicated. Also, in comparison to adults, while young people 16–24 are least likely to say they will drink and drive, they are also least likely to be able to judge their personal safe limits for driving and most likely to claim to be able to drive without their ability being affected (NOP, 1990).

While most young people will not drink and drive, they may ride in a vehicle with an intoxicated driver, despite their intentions not to do so. The survey of 12- to 15-year-olds by Balding *et al.* (1997) found that 70% of this age group intend to avoid being in a car with a driver who has been drinking, with girls being particularly motivated to avoid this (83% compared to 76% of boys). However, an Australian study suggests that the reality of making choices may be different as young people mature, although girls continue to stick to their principles. The study by Mayberry and Clarke (1991) of 240 university students found that over a third had knowingly ridden with a male driver who was over the legal alcohol limit (50 mg %). Most of the passengers believed that it was safe to ride if they thought the driver's ability to drive was not unduly affected by his drinking. However, assessment of the driver's ability was affected by the amount of alcohol that the passenger had consumed. There was a tendency for male students to believe that there were times when they had no other way of getting home, whereas young women believed it was against their principles to ride in a vehicle with an intoxicated male driver (Mayberry and Clarke, 1991).

ATTITUDES TO DESIGNER DRINKS AND ALCOPOPS

Recent studies examining the impact of the introduction of new alcoholic beverages on young people's drinking have established that young people have positive attitudes to the new drinks. Hughes *et al.* (1997) combined qualitative and quantitative methods to examine the appeal of designer drinks to young people in the West of Scotland. The qualitative research found that young people's attitudes to alcoholic beverages varied with age, reflecting their attitudes towards and motivations for drinking in general. Children aged 12–13 used alcohol to experience the adult world, to satisfy their curiosity, to socialise and to say that they had tried drinking. Young people aged 14–15 used alcohol to test their own limits and have fun; drinking to get drunk was important to them, as was sharing the experience with others. By 16–17, young people were keen to demonstrate their maturity and experience of drinking and adopted an adult drinking pattern.

The drinks consumed matched these attitudes and motivations: 12- to 13-year-olds experimented with any available drinks; 14- to 15-year-olds chose strong, cheap and pleasant tasting drinks and found the brand image of designer drinks appealing. The 16- to 17-year-olds had started to develop a taste for a wider range of spirits and bottled beers. They rejected many designer drinks as immature. However, quantitative research found that the same age group (12–17) perceived the market leader designer drink, Mad Dog 20/20, to be appealing in terms of sweet, pleasant taste and affordability. It was also thought to be popular with people their own age and unpopular with people their parents' age. Given a hypothetical choice of drinks including soft, energy and alcoholic drinks, Mad Dog 20/20 appealed most to 13- to 15-year-olds. In contrast, beer consistently increased in popularity with age.

The HEA's survey of attitudes and behaviour towards new types of alcoholic drinks in England (Raw and McNeill, 1997) also found that the new types of alcoholic drinks were more appealing to 11- to 18-year-olds than to 20- to 25-year-olds. Prompted awareness of the new drinks was high, especially alcopops, with over 80% of the 11- to 18-year-olds knowing of them. Both awareness and liking the taste of alcopops peaked at 15 to 16 years. Respondents were shown photographs of different drinks and invited to select phrases from a given list, which applied to that kind of drink. Contrasting alcopops with ordinary beer, lager and cider, 11- to 18-year-olds saw alcopops as more refreshing, better tasting, less likely to taste of alcohol, trendier and suitable for teenage girls. The teenage group also thought the new, strong, fruit-flavoured wines tasted better and were less likely to taste of alcohol than traditional wines or wine/spirit mixtures, for example Malibu. The older respondents were more likely to describe traditional drinks as tasting good and as something to drink with friends at parties.

Teenagers saw strong cider as something to drink with friends at parties, while strong lager was a drink for lads/men. These drinks, plus test tube cocktails and fruit-flavoured wine-based drinks were all rated as getting you drunk quickly by teenagers.

A key conclusion of these studies is that young people choose alcoholic drinks that are consistent with their attitudes to drinking and their alcohol expectancies. The new range of drinks are appealing to teenagers, particularly to those in their mid-teens.

ATTITUDES TO PUBS AND OTHER PLACES TO DRINK

Young people are much more likely to drink in pubs than people over 35. In 1991, to inform its Drinkwise campaign theme on the on-trade (drinking in licensed premises), the HEA commissioned a telephone survey of over 1000 adults, to find out their views on drinking in pubs. When asked what makes a good pub, the 15–24 age group, in common with all other ages, think that 'atmosphere', good ventilation, alcoholic drinks, comfortable seating, soft drinks and decor are important (chosen by over 80% of the sample). In comparison with other ages, atmosphere and music are particularly important features to young people, whereas good ventilation, comfortable seats and food, tea and coffee are less important.

With regard to things about pubs that are disliked, young people share other pub users' dislike of smoke/bad ventilation and loutish/bad behaviour or an unfriendly atmosphere. They are much more likely than any other age group to dislike pubs that are too crowded and less likely to object to loud music or jukeboxes (BMRB, 1991).

These quantitative findings were confirmed by a qualitative study by Gofton (1990) of young city centre pub users. He found that the decor, music, style and atmosphere of pubs were important to young people.

The significance of the pub to young people was also explored in an innovative research project in Tameside, Greater Manchester (Tierney, Cohen and Bates, 1991). Here, the aim was to inform a local response to youthful drinking by asking young people, publicans, youth workers and the police for their views on why young people use pubs, the problems that result and how these might be minimised. Reasons given by young people for going into pubs were most commonly to socialise, meet people and to drink alcohol. Other reasons were to have a good time, enjoyment, atmosphere, because there was nowhere else to go, to get drunk, music, entertainment and to relax. When asked what activities they would like to see available in pubs, the responses indicated an interest in a broad range of activities and services such as discos, later opening, live music, food and hot drinks, games and information. Nearly 80% of those interviewed had experienced problems associated with going into pubs, with violent incidents being experienced by half of the sample.

VIEWS ON PUBLIC POLICY

As well as being more tolerant of drunkenness, young people have rather less interest than older people do in stricter controls on alcohol sales, advertising or taxation. Not surprisingly, they are particularly unlikely to support proposals affecting their own drinking behaviour. A 1994 HEA survey of public attitudes towards alcohol policy measures (MORI, 1994) found that 15- to 24-year-olds share the strong general public support for unit labelling of cans and bottles of alcoholic beverages (96% agree) and for compulsory training courses for publicans and licensees on the law regarding alcohol and their responsibilities to the customer (81% agree).

These are measures that would demand little change in young people's drinking habits.

Those aged 15–24 also echo the general public's views on alcohol taxation and are particularly likely to oppose measures that would increase the price of alcohol. While the majority would favour a uniform tax on alcohol throughout the European community (60% agree), most feel that this should be achieved by the tax in Great Britain being brought *down* to be in line with other European countries, thus reducing the price of alcohol (81% agree). The introduction of higher taxes on stronger alcoholic drinks receives little public support and young people are least likely to support this measure (21% of 15–24s agree compared with 29% overall). Because income is an important factor limiting consumption among the young, they are unlikely to support any measures which increase the price of alcohol.

Young people's attitudes to safe places to drink have important implications for policy on the policing of under-age drinking, according to a study commissioned by the Portman Group (Fox, 1997). Nine panel group discussions with young people aged 10–17 in the main regions of Great Britain found that they considered places to be 'safe' if they were unlikely to be detected by parents or the police, rather than the conventional (adult) concept of safety from harm. Thus the pub was considered 'safe' only for young people who looked 18, while 'back streets and behind buildings' came high on the list of 'safe' places, followed by 'parks/public places', bus stops and toilets. The author suggests that zero tolerance policing of under-age drinking therefore runs the risk of driving children to seek out places to drink which, while being 'safe' in their terms, are clearly not without risk from harm.

The same panel groups also considered alcohol policy issues. These findings confirmed that young people tend to hold liberal attitudes to controls on alcohol misuse, with the exception of drinking and driving, as noted above under 'Attitudes to drinking and driving'. Their views on tackling under-age drinking were particularly interesting. Panellists were invited to suggest ideas for tackling under-age alcohol misuse, which were then voted on by the group. Proposals involving stricter legislation and tougher policing were rejected, while the more liberal proposals obtained the most votes. Winning proposals all contained one of two elements –

lowering the legal drinking age to 16 and more/better alcohol education. The researcher notes a tendency for young people to support tough measures in theory, but to reject any application of these to their own behaviour and suggests that young people may suffer from 'regulation fatigue'. Young people's responses to an alcohol by-law sign prohibiting public drinking indicate that this might make them go somewhere else to drink but would not deter them from drinking. Two-thirds of panellists did not think they would actually get caught if they were drinking near the by-law sign. A 'Cops in Shops' warning poster was also not considered to be a deterrent to buying alcohol and again two-thirds did not believe that it was likely they would be detected. Neither initiative was particularly salient to the panellists, eliciting little concern or interest or attention (Fox, 1997).

Another study commissioned by the Portman Group finds that young people who participate in one of the group's own control measures, the proof of age card scheme, hold positive attitudes towards it. No information is provided about the attitudes of non-users of the scheme (Walker, 1997). A self-completion postal questionnaire survey of 800 recent applicants for the proof of age card across Great Britain found that, at least among card users, there is considerable peer group acceptance. Three-quarters of respondents had friends who had a card and 84% had suggested to friends that they should get one. Respondents were equally divided in opinions about whether or not proof of age cards should be compulsory. Two-thirds agreed that they did not mind being asked to prove their age, although 40% said it was embarrassing to admit you don't look your age; 84% of cardholders agreed that having a proof of age card made them feel more confident when they went out. Agreement was higher among females (87%) than males (78%), those who had completed full-time education before age 18 (91%) and those who had applied because they thought that they 'didn't look their age'. As this study only surveyed cardholders, it cannot be concluded that young people in general support this scheme. The same study also obtained feedback on the proof of age card from managers of three national chains of off-licences that promote the scheme. Again the fact that all respondents currently participated in the scheme limits generalisability of the findings to all off-licence managers. While the majority of managers (84%) agreed that proof of age cards should be compulsory and nine out of ten managers liked having the card application forms available, 82%

also thought the scheme had made no difference to the number of attempts to purchase alcohol made by under 18s.

Young people hold rather less strong views than adults on moral issues such as sponsorship and advertising, and on controls of the availability of alcohol (MORI, 1994). The 15–24 age group are least likely to support a ban on advertising of alcoholic drinks on television (16% of 15–24s agree compared with 28% overall) or a ban on sports sponsorship by the alcohol industry (17% of 15–24s agree compared with 23% overall). While the majority of young people would *not* support the sale of alcohol by convenience stores in petrol stations, there is greater support in this age group than any other (17% agree, compared with 9% overall).

ATTITUDES OF YOUNG PEOPLE FROM MINORITY ETHNIC GROUPS

The ethnic group to which young people belong has been largely ignored in attitude studies, yet the available evidence suggests that there are major differences according to ethnic group. A study of 'Asian' and white school children (13–16 years) in Glasgow (Kohli, 1989) found that Asians (defined as people of Indian, Pakistani or Bangladeshi descent) held significantly more negative attitudes to alcohol than white schoolchildren of the same age. Asians were much more likely to disagree that 'drinking is a normal thing to do' (67% of Asians disagree, compared to 47% of white children), 'drinking makes you feel at ease' (49% of Asians disagreed, compared to 33% of white children) and that 'drinking is only bad if you drink a lot' (half the Asians disagreed compared with a quarter of white children).

The HEA's Health Behaviour of Schoolchildren survey of 1995 (Turtle, Jones and Hickman, 1997) included a second sample to represent the ethnic communities resident in England. Non-white children in both the main sample and the second 'ethnic' sample held less liberal and tolerant attitudes to alcohol than white schoolchildren. In the main sample, non-white children were more likely than white pupils to agree that they liked soft drinks more than alcohol (85% compared with 72%) and less likely to enjoy the taste of alcoholic drinks (28% compared with 58%). They were much more likely to agree that nobody under age 18 should be allowed to drink (66% compared with 38%). They were also less likely than white peers to agree that drinking alcohol had personal or social benefits, as shown in Table 9.

Table 9 Attitudes to statements by ethnicity

Those agreeing	Main sample		Ethnic schools sample		
	White %	Non-white %	White %	Black %	Asian %
I feel more confident when I have a drink	30	13	21	8	10
Life is more fun when you have a drink	29	14	20	14	11
It is easier to make friends when you have a drink	19	10	13	6	8

Source: Turtle, Jones and Hickman (1996)

In the ethnic schools sample, black pupils were more likely than Asian to like the taste of alcohol (29% agreed, compared with 11%) and less likely to agree that under-18s should not be allowed to drink (59% compared with 76%).

The HEA also studied the appropriateness and delivery of the 'sensible drinking' message to adults who drank alcohol, from black and minority ethnic groups living in England (HEA, 1994). Much of the information is from small samples and is not broken down by age, so the views of young people cannot be identified. It should also be noted that these are views of South Asian, African and Caribbean people who drink alcohol and they will therefore not be representative of the general views of young people from ethnic groups where drinking is rare, for example among Muslims. General opinions on drinking alcohol were split between three age groups, with those aged over 44 being generally negative and those aged 25–44 having a generally positive opinion. Young people aged 16–24 are ambivalent about drinking. 'Moderation', if approved of at all, is interpreted as meaning not showing drunken behaviour, rather than having any link with consumption levels.

With regard to the effects of alcohol, young drinkers from South Asian, African and Caribbean backgrounds share the expectancies of their white peers, that alcohol will make you feel good and help you to relax. Reasons given for drinking are also the same as those given by white young adults – socialising and relaxation. Looking at who the respondents perceive to be the main drinkers in their own community, younger men are most mentioned by the Africans, Muslims and Hindus. Caribbeans and Sikhs think that older men are the main drinkers in their communities. In general, female drinking, even among young women, is considerably less socially acceptable in these minority ethnic communities.

As with studies of young people's behaviour, we know relatively little about the alcohol-related attitudes and values held by young people from minority ethnic groups. TACADE's alcohol education project with Asian young women in Bedford suggests that their experience of growing up in a predominantly white culture where drinking is the norm is considerably different to the experience of their white peers. Their attitudes to alcohol were less tolerant than those of their white friends (Wright and Buczkiewicz, 1995). The HEA's qualitative study of young drinkers highlights important differences in the place and meaning of drinking among white, African, Caribbean, Hindu and Muslim young drinkers (Mathrani, 1998). More research is needed into the place and meaning of alcohol among young people from minority ethnic groups.

ATTITUDES TO ALCOHOL EDUCATION IN SCHOOLS

When young people are asked whether or not they agree with lists of statements about the desirability of more, or better alcohol education, they will readily agree (Fox, 1997, Coffield and Gofton, 1994). However, few studies have attempted to determine whether this reflects young people's genuine felt needs or whether such statements are loaded in such a way as to make it hard to disagree! The Portman Group's panel discussions found that in relation to other influences on their drinking, young people considered that teachers had virtually no influence at all, either on attitudes or behaviour (Fox, 1997). All sources of information were mediated by the peer group, with choices being made that were favoured or approved by the immediate circle of friends. The majority of panellists perceived the formal alcohol education message as disapproval – drinking is wrong, naughty or bad.

The HEA's HBSC survey found that despite the inclusion of alcohol and drug education within the English national curriculum for schools, only 58% of secondary-school children say they have covered sensible drinking or alcohol at school, rising from 34% in year 7 to 76% in year 11. Of seven health topics that were included the government's Health of the Nation strategy, alcohol comes sixth in schoolchildren's recall of having had lessons at school, after sex education, exercise, food and diet, smoking and drugs. Only HIV/AIDS is less frequently covered according to young people. Furthermore, young people do not particularly want to have more lessons on the subject – only 39% want this, with demand diminishing as they get older (43% at year 7, 33% at year 11). Drugs and sex education are the main subjects young people want to know about (Turtle, Jones and Hickman, 1997).

4. Marketing and advertising alcohol

SUMMARY

1. Whether advertising causes people, particularly young people, to start drinking, or to continue or increase their consumption has been hotly debated. There is some evidence to suggest a small but significant positive association between young people's exposure to alcohol advertisements, their consumption levels and positive attitudes to alcohol. Further evidence is needed to establish whether the new alcoholic drinks introduced in the last decade encourage more young people to start to drink, or young drinkers to drink more.

2. The 'advertising response function' model explains the general relationship between alcohol advertising and consumption and supports the view that advertising at local level significantly increases consumption.

3. The new designer drinks and alcopops have been successfully labelled, packaged and marketed to appeal to young people. There is considerable evidence that the new drinks appeal to young people, and appeal more to teenagers than those legally entitled to purchase them.

4. British studies have found that young people like, enjoy and remember alcohol advertisements, particularly those shown on television. However, adolescents, including 10- to 13-year-olds, are capable of sophisticated interpretations of the messages, images and targeting of alcohol advertisements, in the same way as adults.

5. Monitoring of alcohol advertisements in the North West of England concluded that two-thirds of the 21 advertisements viewed broke the Advertising Standards code in some way. Half were judged to be aimed at young people and a third featured someone aged under 25.

6. Neither the Advertising Standards code nor the drinks industry's voluntary system of regulation on the packaging and marketing of alcopops seems to be working effectively.

7. Alcohol education can teach young people to resist persuasive alcohol advertising appeals.

*

THE EFFECTS OF ADVERTISING

In reviewing public policy on alcohol, Griffith Edwards and colleagues (1994) have pointed out that alcohol has been one of the world's most heavily advertised products over the past two decades, despite the many restrictions placed on it because of public health concerns. In the United Kingdom, £189.5 million was spent in 1996 on promoting alcohol (Alcohol Concern, 1997b).

Whether advertising causes people, particularly young people, to start drinking, or to continue or increase their consumption has been hotly debated. The marketing, advertising and packaging of the new alcoholic drinks, including alcopops, are a particular focus of concern in the 1990s. Advertising of all kinds is part of the world in which young people grow up and can have a positive role in providing information and increasing consumer choice. On the other hand, the alcohol industry would not invest such huge sums of money unless it expected advertising to sell its products. The alcohol industry argues that advertising purely promotes brand preference rather than encouraging alcohol consumption *per se*. Other potential effects of advertising, which are relevant to health promotion aimed at young people, might be to influence social norms regarding youthful drinking and/or reinforce young people's positive attitudes to drinking or starting to drink (Edwards *et al.*, 1994), or even to question adults' moral disapproval of young people's drinking.

Internationally, research on the effects on alcohol consumption and on indices of alcohol misuse has produced mixed results. Reviewing the literature, Saffer (1996) suggests that an economic model underlying the general relationship between advertising and consumption can help explain the varied findings. The 'advertising response function' model has been applied to various products, from lemonade to biscuits to illustrate the effect that different levels of advertising have on product consumption. The model predicts that consumption increases as advertising levels rise, with the rate of increase in consumption eventually tapering off at very high levels of advertising. Saffer points out that this explains why studies using national data on overall alcohol advertising expenditure in all market sectors, have tended to show little or no relationship to national alcohol consumption. Such studies measure advertising at a high level, which varies minimally from year to year. At this high level the model predicts little or no effect on alcohol consumption. In contrast, studies that use local level data over the course of a year find wide variation in the level of advertising and, as the model predicts, tend to conclude that alcohol advertising significantly increases consumption. Studies of advertising bans show a decrease in alcohol consumption and in indices of alcohol abuse (Saffer, 1991). Counter advertising likewise reduces alcohol consumption (Saffer, 1996).

In reviewing the effects of commercial advertising on young people, Edwards *et al.* (1994) draw attention to the methodological limitations of early empirical research, which mainly used laboratory-type experimental situations to measure impact. Such studies have typically shown a short-term impact of alcohol advertising on young people's consumption. American cross-sectional studies of young people's self-reported exposure to advertising and their reported drinking behaviour have also shown small but significant relationships between exposure to advertising and young people's consumption of alcohol and their attitudes to it. For example, Edwards *et al.* (1994) cite Strickland's data (1983) on American teenagers which suggest that a 5-minute increase in exposure to alcohol advertisements (that's a lot of adverts!) was associated with a 5 g (over half a unit) increase in daily consumption of alcohol. American studies have also looked at the impact of advertising on children and adolescents who have not yet started to drink regularly. A recent study has found that children who can identify more beer advertisements hold more favourable beliefs about alcohol and intend to drink more when they become drinkers (Grube and Wallack, 1994).

A New Zealand longitudinal study (Connolly *et al.*, 1994) of young men from age 13 through to 18 has found a significant relationship between the number of alcohol advertisements they recall at 13, and the amount of alcohol they drink at 18. The frequency of drinking is not related, but young men who remember more advertising (mainly television adverts for beer) report drinking more beer on single occasions.

In the USA, youth exposure to beer advertising most often comes during television sports programming (Grube and Wallack, 1994). Slater *et al.* (1996a) found that American white, male adolescents consistently preferred beer advertisements with sports content to those without sports content. However, they found no evidence to support concerns that sports programming might prime young people to be more receptive to alcohol advertising.

British studies have found that young people like, enjoy and remember alcohol advertisements, particularly those shown on television. As part of a larger survey on children's smoking and advertising (Nelson and White, 1992), over 7000 pupils aged 11–16 from 10 schools in the North, South and Midlands of England were asked what their favourite advertisement was, why the liked it and where they had seen it. Most pupils (91%) had a favourite advertisement and virtually all had seen it on television (96%) compared with 15% in a magazine or on a poster and 5% in a newspaper. Of 17 different categories of consumer products, beer and lager advertisements were the most popular favourites with boys of all ages and their popularity increased with age. Confectionery and soft drinks were most popular favourites for girls, with beer or lager advertisements taking third place (but second place for 11- to 12-year-old girls). Gender differences suggested important differences in personal priorities. Girls were significantly more likely than boys to favour advertisements for food, sweets, soft drinks, toiletries and detergents and clothes. Boys were significantly more likely to favour those for beer and lager, cigars, computers and cars. Humour was the commonest reason given by both sexes for liking an advertisement, and was particularly important to boys. Girls, especially the 15- to 16-year-olds, were significantly more likely than boys to say they liked the person(s) in the advertisement and 13- to 16-year-old girls especially liked the music. Young people whose favourite advertisement was for alcohol or tobacco products were significantly more likely to choose it because it was humorous.

In this study, drinking behaviour was simply classified in terms of drinking beer or lager 'never', 'sometimes' or 'often'. Drinkers were more likely to choose advertisements for beer or lager. Young people who said they drank beer or lager 'often' were more likely than those who 'never' drank or 'occasional' drinkers to say they 'liked the product'.

Studies conducted in Strathclyde (Hastings, MacKintosh and Aitken, 1992), on the perception of alcohol advertising with a similar age group (10- to 16-year-olds), using qualitative and quantitative methods, confirmed young people's general liking for alcohol advertising and the importance of humour to them. These studies found that the younger pupils disapproved of the products displayed but enjoyed the comedy and excitement portrayed. By 14, boys were adopting a more 'cynical' and sophisticated view, finding the appeals to masculinity, sociability and working-class values especially attractive. Comparing drinkers and non-drinkers, drinkers had been exposed to more alcohol advertisements and were more aware and appreciative of them. The Strathclyde studies also found that adolescents including 10- to 13-year-olds are capable of sophisticated interpretations of the messages, images and targeting of alcohol advertisements, in the same way as adults. The authors note that alcohol advertisements seem to be 'finely tuned' to the lifestyles and aspirations of the young respondents, despite the restriction of the Advertising Standards code!

MARKETING DRINKS IN THE 1990s

As discussed in Chapter 1 (see 'Beverage preferences: What do young people choose to drink?), further evidence is needed to establish whether the new alcoholic drinks introduced in the last decade encourage more young people to start to drink, or young drinkers to drink more. There is considerable evidence that the new drinks appeal to young people, and appeal more to young teenagers than to those legally entitled to purchase them (Hughes *et al.*, 1997; Raw and McNeill, 1997; McNeill *et al.*, in preparation).

Apart from their high alcoholic strength, the main feature which distinguishes the new drinks from traditional alcoholic beverages is the way they are marketed and packaged (McNeill *et al.*, in preparation).

These tactics recognise the interests, aspirations, imagery and social behaviour of young people. Most of these drinks are marketed without advertising, thus avoiding the strictures of the Advertising Standards code. Alcohol Concern (1996a) notes that no alcopops were advertised until October 1995:

> 'promotions in pubs and clubs during a hot summer provided enough exposure to ensure high sales. Subsequent advertising was via posters on buses and hoardings, appropriate for catching the attention of a young on-the-move audience. Many off-licences used blackboard advertisements... Much has been achieved by word-of-mouth recommendations, almost turning some of the products into cult drinks, thus ensuring that they fit in with the overall ethics of youth culture.' (p. 9)

Packaging and labelling of the new drinks use images, words and symbols which fit very obviously into youth culture. Packaging is brightly coloured, bold and striking, some drinks have glow in the dark labels and containers include odd, gimmicky shapes including sticks of dynamite, syringes and test-tubes. The names and images are colourful and rebellious, incorporating many that are associated with risk, 'buzz' and illicit drug use. Whitbread's analysis of the new drinks market for their distributors, while taking care not to specifically mention under-18s, acknowledges the intention to address a youth market:

> 'There is a fundamental change in the types of products that 18–24 year olds want to drink. They are rejecting traditional alcohol drinks and are looking for different experiences – the range of alcohol bases and flavours offered by flavoured alcoholic beverages (FABs) meets this need.' (Whitbread, 1996)

'Sector definition chart:

1. *Buzz drinks* include revitalising ingredients, e.g. guarana, ginseng. Unisex drinking profile. Similar age profile to alcoholic sodas, linked to dancing and music. Occasion based – focused on the "big night out".

2. *Alcoholic sodas* (aka alcopops). Fruit and carbonated. Female drinker base (56% female, 44% male). Young drinker (41% are 18–24).

3. *Spirit mixers* Male bias (52% male). Older drinker profile, 42% are 21–29. Sophisticated packaging; drier, more challenging taste.

4. *Cider/beer mixtures* Profile depends on the product.
Cider mixtures – young female bias. Beer mixtures – older male bias. These drinks are more traditional with low consumer interest.'

(Whitbread, 1996)

In 1996, in response to growing criticism of the rising alcopop market, the Portman Group issued a *voluntary* code on the naming, packaging and merchandising of alcoholic drinks. This code was further tightened up in May 1997. This voluntary system of regulation appears to be having a limited effect, although the threat of compulsory regulation does seem to be having some impact on packaging. The majority of complaints submitted to the Portman Group by Alcohol Concern are not upheld (Alcohol Concern, 1997b) and some of those that are upheld by the Portman Group, are not acted on by the drinks manufacturers. No doubt this debate will rumble on for some time. It may be influenced by the conclusions of a Ministerial Group which is currently examining this issue as part of a broader consideration of problems related to young people's drinking.

Clearly alcohol advertising and alcohol product marketing in Britain is getting through to children and is communicating appealing messages to them. The Advertising Standards code appears to provide limited protection against inappropriate or unbalanced messages. Monitoring of alcohol advertisements by a panel of adult volunteers in the North West of England concluded that two-thirds of the 21 advertisements viewed broke the Advertising Standards code in some way. Half were judged to be aimed at young people and a third featured someone aged under 25. Other transgressions were the implication of social acceptance and sexual success and links with masculinity (Pendleton, Smith and Roberts, 1988).

Images portrayed by non-commercial television programmes have also been monitored and criticised as presenting a biased picture in favour of drinking alcohol, especially wine-drinking. Portrayal of alcohol on prime time television in Britain was monitored in 1983 (Hansen, 1984) and in 1986 (Smith, Roberts and Pendleton, 1988), the latter exercise being part of the HEA funded Drink Wisely North West campaign. The 1986 survey found little change in three years, with 4 out of 5 prime-time television programmes making visual or verbal reference to alcohol. Averaging one reference to alcohol to every 6 minutes, the programmes showed more alcohol being consumed than soft drinks or beverages (in contrast to real life).

Contrary to published programming guidelines about care in exposing children to alcohol references, prevalence of alcohol was equally spread throughout prime-time television, including half the programmes starting before 6.30 p.m. Even programmes with television audience ratings of over 20% of under-16s contained an average of 15 references to alcohol per hour.

Despite the HEA's success in placing a 'Drinkwise' ice bucket in the pub featured in the television series *EastEnders*, non-alcoholic drinks fared badly with product placement, in comparison to alcoholic beverages. A skewed image of alcoholic drinks consumption was also portrayed, with wines and spirits shown more often than beer. There were few references to the hazards of alcohol consumption. The most frequent references were to intoxication, which were often presented in a humorous or light-hearted way.

While the evidence gives some support to the view that alcohol advertising and the portrayal of alcohol on television is reaching young people and is reinforcing their drinking, its impact should be kept in perspective. It is encouraging that young people do seem to be aware of advertising messages and of the subtle pressures they impose. In reviewing the current evidence, Hastings, MacKintosh and Aitken (1992) suggest that advertising has less influence on young people's drinking than other factors such as the family, peers, social settings and cultural norms.

Moreover, an American study provides evidence that alcohol education can teach young people to resist persuasive alcohol advertising appeals. Slater *et al.* (1996b) found that recent exposure to alcohol education classes in general, and discussion of alcohol advertising in those classes were both positively associated with young people's ability to produce spontaneous counter-arguments to alcohol advertisements. In relation to current concern about designer drinks and alcopops this finding suggests that developing young people's skills appraisal of advertising, marketing and product imagery should feature in alcohol education programmes.

5. The influence of parents and peers

SUMMARY

1. Cross-sectional studies consistently show that young people who drink tend to have friends who drink, while those who do not drink tend to have friends who also do not drink.

2. Interpretations of peer group pressure as an explanation for young people's drinking behaviour can equally be viewed as evidence for peer association: young people choose to associate with others whose drinking habits are like their own.

3. Young people are by no means a homogenous group and different peer groups have different drinking cultures.

4. Children and young people are vulnerable to the effects of adults' drinking, particularly parents. Vulnerability includes the direct toxic effect of alcohol on the foetus during pregnancy and indirect effects mediated through other aspects of family life and the social environment.

5. Children of parents who are problem drinkers experience a wide range of problems, most of which are not solely or directly due to alcohol. Problems include emotional and behavioural disorders and low self-esteem. In adolescence this may be manifested as poor educational performance, anxiety, depression, social isolation or anti-social behaviour.

6. The impact of a parental drink problem is strongest in young children and less certain in adolescents.

7. Protective factors which reduce the negative impact of a parental problem drinker on a child are: a close loving relationship with a

103

parent or someone outside the immediate family, a resilient personality and high achievement in some field, for example school, sport, hobby.

8. Family support and cohesion are associated with positive outcomes for young adults, whether or not there is a drink problem in the family. Family life is an important influence on adolescent drinking.

9. Four family socialisation factors – support, control, models and parental attitudes, are independently and additively related to adolescent drinking behaviour, with young people's perceptions of parental attitudes being the most salient factor. The optimal family life for producing sensible drinking among young people seems to be a family that offers moderate levels of support and control, attitudes that support sensible drinking by young people and a model of sensible parental drinking.

10. Parents and peers may exert different types of influence on young people's alcohol use and the pattern may vary for males and females, according to the results of an Australian study. Replicative studies are required to establish the direction and degree of influence of parents and peers in relation to the drinking behaviour of young people in Britain.

*

THE PEER GROUP

It is commonly held that once young people reach adolescence, the importance of family influences decline and young people's behaviour is increasingly influenced by the behaviour of their peers. Peer group pressure is a frequently cited explanation for adolescent drinking. Recently, British researchers have criticised both the moral values that underpin this theory and the empirical evidence that supports it (May, 1993). Davies (1992) has pointed out that peer group pressure tends to be used to explain behaviours of which adults disapprove; it is less commonly advanced in support of approved activities:

'it appears to me that the peer group explanation has become little
more than a way of identifying with ... "good kids" who do things we
don't like. In such circumstances we attribute their behaviour to
"wicked others".'
                                                                    (pp. 29–32)

The importance of the peer group has been derived from cross-sectional
studies, which consistently show that young people who drink tend to
have friends who drink, while those who do not drink tend to have
friends who also do not drink (Iannotti, Bush and Weinfurt, 1996).
However, this *association* does not necessarily imply causality and there
have been relatively few longitudinal studies which might shed light on
the direction of the influence. Despite the data limitations, researchers
have overwhelmingly chosen to interpret the association as evidence to
support the notion of peer group influence. Coggans and McKellar (1994)
suggest that this is because alternative explanations simply do not fit with
the prevailing moral disapproval of young people's drinking. It is more
comfortable to look for evidence that drinking is not the fault of the
young person, who has been led astray by others, than to consider other
possibilities, for example that young people might enjoy drinking alcohol
and choose to associate with others who hold the same views.

Both Davies (1992) and Coggans and McKellar (1994) present a
convincing argument that interpretations of *peer pressure* or *peer
influence* should more appropriately be viewed as evidence for *peer
preference* or *peer association*. In other words, young people choose to
associate with others whose drinking habits are like their own. Iannotti,
Bush and Weinfurt (1996) conducted a four-year, longitudinal study (in
the USA) which supports the peer association explanation. They found
that perceived friends' substance use (alcohol, tobacco and marijuana) is
more likely to be a *product* of an adolescent's previous substance use than
a precursor of subsequent use.

This reinterpretation argues that far from being passive recipients of peer
influence, young people are active players, who choose to drink in certain
ways because this behaviour meets (or they believe it to meet) their needs.
Social influences do exist; in constructing meanings related to drinking
and managing their social worlds, young people behave within the rules
and norms set by the groups to which they belong – but the relationship is
two-way. For example, several American studies have found that young

people's drinking habits are more closely related to their perceptions about their friends' drinking than to objective measures or self-reports of friends' actual drinking (Iannottti, Bush and Weifurt, 1996; Wilks, Callan and Austin, 1989; Iannotti and Bush, 1992).

Most of the recent British qualitative studies of young people's drinking support the view that there is a dynamic relationship between individual self-determination and social group influences. These studies also identify the friendship group(s) in which young people do their drinking as the focus of this dynamic, rather than the wider group of schoolmates or other peers (Mathrani, 1998; Gofton, 1990; Brain and Parker, 1997; Fox, 1997).

The qualitative studies also indicate that different groups of young people have very different drinking cultures, as contrasted by observations of young city centre pub users in the North East (Gofton, 1990), Asian young women in Bedford (Wright and Buczkiewicz, 1995), 14- to 15-year-olds and young street drinkers in the North West (Newcombe, Measham and Parker, 1995; Brain and Parker, 1997). Furthermore, few young people are members of only one drinking group and they will move into other group settings as they mature. The social context for drinking will also have an impact on their drinking behaviour, so that a group will drink in different ways depending on the circumstances and environment.

Qualitative work in the UK (Dorn, 1983; Gofton, 1990; Mathrani, 1998; Pavis, Cunningham-Burleys and Amos, 1997; Dean, 1990), in the USA (Glassner and Loughlin, 1987) and in New Zealand (Wylie and Casswell 1991), and ethnographic studies elsewhere (McDonald, 1994) highlight the fact that adolescent drinking is socially organised. Drinking behaviour is subject to a set of 'rules' which regulate and structure that behaviour within a specific situation. Youthful that cultures in turn reflect the wider social and cultural environment within which they are located.

These conclusions have important implications for health promotion. If peer pressure is an inadequate explanation of young people's drinking, it follows that prevention programmes based on resistance to peer pressure will have little success; their evaluation to date would seem to confirm this, though some success has been found in relation to smoking (Coggans *et al.*, 1991).

ALCOHOL AND FAMILY LIFE

There are two ways that young people may experience alcohol-related harm. The first relates to risks attached to their own drinking behaviour (see Chapter 6). The second is the negative effects of adults' drinking behaviour, particularly those of parents. This second element of alcohol-related harm rarely seems to attract the same amount of public concern or media interest as the moral protestations surrounding youthful intoxication or public drunkenness, although it has attracted some research interest. However, the value of the data is limited, because many of the studies are North American, and most examine the children of parents who are diagnosed as problem drinkers or 'alcoholics' and are in contact with treatment services. Relatively few studies have involved families derived from general population samples. A literature review (Shucksmith, 1994) on the effects of parental alcohol misuse on children also noted that studies mostly adopted a pathological approach, with the assumption that the effects must be negative in all cases. The experiences and perceptions of children and young people themselves, their 'voice', were largely absent from the literature, which relied on external measures of children's performance, adults' accounts or clinical generalisations (but see later account of work by Laybourn, Brown and Hill, 1996).

The negative effects of adults' drinking are different at different times in a child's life. Exposure to alcohol during pregnancy, particularly during the early weeks, can have a toxic effect on the developing foetus. Rarely and most seriously this can cause foetal alcohol syndrome (FAS); the precise mechanisms are unknown, as are the level and frequency of alcohol consumption which might produce it. FAS is more commonly found in babies of women diagnosed as alcohol dependent and is mediated by social, environmental and nutritional factors. Children with FAS perform poorly at school and show an extremely high rate of psychiatric disorders (Royal College of Physicians, 1995).

After birth, the effects of adults' drinking on children and young people are both direct and indirect, mediated through other aspects of family life and the wider social environment. Adult problem drinkers frequently have other underlying problems, for example difficult personalities or marriage problems, which may modify the impact of alcohol. Children and young people also have both vulnerability and protective factors such as learning difficulties or physical illness, which will mediate the impact of a family member's drinking upon them. Protective factors that reduce the negative impact of parental problem drinking on young people have been found to include:

- a close, positive, affectionate relationship with one or both parents or someone outside the immediate family (for example grandparent)

- a resilient personality

- high achievement in some field, for example school, sport, hobby.
  (Velleman, 1993; Royal College of Physicians, 1995; Orford, 1990).

Alcohol-related problems are commonly implicated in child abuse, receptions into care and loss of parental rights with respect to children, although not usually as the sole factor (Coleman and Cassell, 1995, Laybourn, Brown and Hill, 1996). Children of 'problem drinkers' display a high rate of emotional and behavioural disorders (West and Prinz, 1987) and tend to have low self-esteem and high levels of anxiety and depression (Royal College of Physicians, 1995). Within the age group covered by this review, they are more likely to suffer from depression or show anti-social conduct disorders such as stealing, lying, aggressive behaviour and truanting. Much of this effect is considered to be due to a link between problem drinking and family disruption, particularly family conflict, divorce or domestic violence (Brisby, Baker and Hedderwick, 1997). On a less dramatic level, frequent intoxication is likely to reduce an adult's abilities to provide consistent care and supervision for children. However, the impact of a carer's heavy drinking may be different for children at different ages; Velleman and Orford (1993) note that it is strongest in young children and less certain in adolescents. They investigated the experiences of young adults aged 16 to 35 who had problem-drinking parents, in comparison with young adults whose parents had not had drink problems. Nearly all the offspring of problem drinkers described negative childhood experiences, yet current differences between the two groups were minimal. In terms of life patterns, satisfaction and coping measures, only a minority were experiencing long-term negative consequences. Persistent problems were most likely when there had been family conflict as well as problem drinking. They conclude that the risks are due more to family disharmony than the direct effects of alcohol. Family support and cohesion was associated with positive outcomes for young adults, whether or not a parent had a drink problem.

The qualitative study of 20 families by Laybourn, Brown and Hill (1996) also confirmed varying impact of adult problem drinking on children of different ages. The problems reported by the secondary-school children and young adults in the families were those noted by other larger studies: educational failure, anti-social behaviour, social isolation, substance misuse and a sense of 'lost childhood'. A number of young adults seemed to be leading positive, sociable lives and a few even identified benefits such as improved coping skills and (as with Velleman and Orford's work) greater family closeness.

The finding that children and young people are not inevitably doomed to dysfunction and difficulty due to problem drinking in families is an important message to communicate. At the same time the distress and hurt experienced warrants appropriate help and support for the children of problem drinkers.

Much of the research on alcohol and family life has been conducted on abnormal populations, where one or more family member is in contact with a service because of an identified drink problem. The findings that in such families, children and young people experience a range of problems are not surprising. Of more interest to health promotion are the factors reported earlier which appear to protect the children of problem drinkers, and the general impact of family life (where there is no known drink problem) in promoting sensible drinking among young people.

Parental attitudes and behaviour do play an important part in the development of their children's behaviour. Appropriate modelling of sensible drinking by parents seems to be important, as both abstainers and heavy drinkers are more likely to have heavy drinking children (McKechnie *et al.*, 1977; Orford, 1990). One small qualitative study of written comments about drinking and family life, made by twenty 15- to 16-year-olds in one school class, found that this group saw their drinking as normal, unproblematic and sanctioned by their parents. Their statements highlighted the importance of family influence, particularly parental consent, and appropriate parental and family drinking as key factors in sensible drinking. The young people also identified the negative influence on their drinking of poor family relationships and inappropriate parental drinking (Foxcroft, Lowe and May, 1994).

Foxcroft and Lowe (1991) conducted a meta-analysis of research studies that had examined drinking behaviour and family behaviour. Three factors recurred in the literature: family support, family control and family structure. All three dimensions of family behaviour were negatively related to adolescent drinking behaviour:

• Adolescents from less supportive families tended to drink more

• Adolescents from less controlling families tended to drink more

• Adolescents from non-nuclear families tended to drink more.

Lowe, Foxcroft and Sibley (1993) also reviewed and conducted a meta-analysis of recent studies of the relationship between adolescent drinking and parental drinking. Their conclusions were that:

• Adolescents drink more if their parents drink more

• Adolescents drink more if their parents approve of their drinking.

Lowe, Foxcroft and Sibley (1993) tested all of these hypotheses concerning the relationship between adolescent drinking and family life by in-depth interviews with teenage volunteers, a large survey of 11- to 18-year-olds in Humberside and a study of 430 YTS trainees aged 16–19. Their conclusions were that the four family socialisation factors were independently and additively related to adolescent drinking behaviour, with young people's perceptions of parental attitudes being the most salient factor (Figure 11).

Pointing out that *non-drinking* as well as heavy drinking is deviant in British adolescents, the authors identified the most favourable family environments for adolescents to develop 'socially competent' drinking behaviour. They found that the family behaviours that consistently socialise an adolescent towards heavier drinking are a combination of low parental support, low parental control, heavy parental drinking and condoning attitudes. The optimal family life for producing sensible drinking among young people seems to be a family which offers moderate levels of support and control, attitudes which support sensible drinking (and do not condone heavy or risky drinking) by young people and a model of sensible parental drinking.

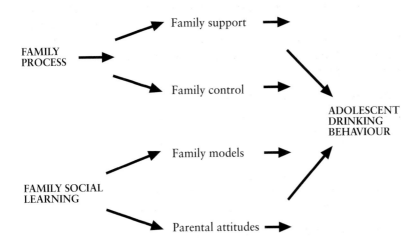

Source: Lowe, Foxcroft and Sibley (1993)

Figure 11 Family socialisation factors which influence the development of adolescent drinking

PARENTS AND PEERS: DIFFERENT TYPES OF INFLUENCE?

Parents and peers may exert different types of influence on young people's alcohol use, and the pattern may vary for males and females, according to the results of an Australian study by Wilks, Callan and Austin (1989). They obtained measures of perceived and actual drinking behaviour and normative standards for drinking behaviour (whether they felt they should drink) from 106 young people (average age 18 for women and 19 for men), their parents and same-sex best friend. The modelling of parents' and best friend's drinking and in particular internalised norms were found especially to influence the drinking of young men. In contrast, for young women, internalised norms did not predict alcohol use and there was a direct modelling effect; how much they believed their best friend drank and their friend's normative standards were the strongest predictors of alcohol use. Fathers' drinking also influenced young women's alcohol consumption but mothers had no impact on their daughter's drinking behaviour. Additionally, personal preferences (measured by the degree to which they said that they enjoyed drinking) predicted most of young women's drinking behaviour, but was not a strong predictor of young men's drinking. These results must be interpreted with caution as the sample was not representative of the general Australian population in this age group and may not accurately describe the influences on young people in Britain. Replication of this study in Britain would be useful, in informing alcohol education messages aimed at young people.

6. Alcohol-related harm: What sort of harm does young people's drinking cause?

SUMMARY

1. In addition to the harm young people experience due to adults' drinking, young people's own drinking is associated with a wide range of risks and harms, although the nature of the relationships is often less well established. The clustering of heavy drinking with other risky behaviour in young people presents difficulties in disentangling the effects of drinking alcohol from other risk factors.

2. The fact that young people are not fully developed means that they face greater risks in using alcohol. Children and adolescents' metabolism of alcohol and their physiological response to intoxication differs from that of adults. Novice young drinkers will experience greater intoxication (for a given amount of alcohol) than regular drinkers, because they will have acquired little physical tolerance to the drug. Young people who weigh less than adults will also achieve a higher blood-alcohol level. Alcohol's depressant effect can more easily produce a fatally toxic overdose in young people.

3. No alcohol problem is exclusive to young people, but there is a discernible pattern of alcohol-related problems. Intoxication, episodic drunkenness or 'binge drinking' are most likely to lead to problems such as violence, crime and accidents. Cancers, heart disease, liver cirrhosis and other health consequences of chronic heavy drinking are rarely seen in young drinkers. Youthful drinking behaviour is not a good predictor of alcohol-related illness or physical dependence in later life.

4. Compared to other age groups, young adults have the highest risk of alcohol dependence and problem drinking, although numerically, problems related to single episodes of intoxication are much more common.

5. Drinking alcohol is a positive experience for most young people. The commonest immediate negative consequences experienced by young drinkers are the physiological responses to alcohol – hangover, nausea, dizziness or falls. Gender differences have been noted in under-18s – young women are more likely to report emotional experiences or negative social consequences, while young men are more likely to report involvement in criminal activities.

6. Accidents are the most important serious negative consequence of young people's drinking. Alcohol is implicated in 20–30% of all accidents. Alcohol is an important contributory factor in facial injuries, especially injuries to young people aged 15–25. Accidents, particularly on the roads and near water, are especially common in the under-25s. Drivers aged under 20 have more accidents than older drivers do, even at blood-alcohol levels below the legal limit, confirming that inexperience in driving and inexperience in drinking are a particularly risky combination. Male drivers in their twenties are the group most likely to fail a breath test or be involved in a drink-driving accident.

7. While alcohol is associated with a wide range of crimes, it is not necessarily the cause of crime. Young people's drinking and offending share common causes rather than drinking causing crime. Young adults (17–24) are known to be the heaviest drinkers in the population and are also the most likely age group to be involved in crime. The rate of convictions for drunkenness peaks at age 18. There is a tendency for most young people to grow out of both types of behaviour, risky drinking and offending, as they reach their mid-20s.

8. While there is ample evidence to implicate alcohol in violent acts, the relationship most strongly supported by the research evidence is that aggressive behaviour is developed early in life and later leads to heavy drinking, especially for young men. Drinking and aggression also have shared antecedents. Alcohol-related violence may have less to do

with alcohol *per se* than with the social context in which people drink, particularly people with aggressive tendencies.

9. How alcohol affects sexual behaviour and whether alcohol use *causes* sexual risk-taking has yet to be established. In the UK, studies suggest a positive *association* between drinking alcohol before sexual activity and not using contraception. Young people *combine* alcohol and sex, especially prior to their first sexual experience. They are more likely than older people to say that emotions influence their drinking and more likely to drink when experiencing positive emotions especially romance and stimulation. The part played by alcohol in sexual risk-taking is bound up in the social rituals, expectancies and meanings placed on drinking and on sex by groups of young people.

10. There is a significant positive correlation between alcohol use and misuse by young people and their use of tobacco and illicit drugs, although little is known of the interrelationships that exist.

*

Chapter 5 reviewed the harm caused to young people by adults' drinking. This chapter considers a second perspective on harm, which is the focus of far more media attention and public anxiety. This is the harm related to young people's own drinking behaviour. As noted in the introduction, concern about young people's use of alcohol may include elements of 'moral panic' (Dorn, 1983) fuelled by sensationalist mass-media accounts of youthful behaviour when intoxicated. Anxiety about public disorder and violence led to the labelling of young male drinkers as 'lager louts' in the 1980s. In the 1990s fear of crime is currently of great public concern and this anxiety is now once again being focused on the young and the part alcohol plays in crime.

A survey of youth workers in England, Wales and Northern Ireland found that they were concerned about the potential harm that young people could experience or cause to others as a result of drinking. Their most frequently expressed concerns were about violence, crime (especially vandalism and damage), accidents/injury, drink driving harm, sexual risks, alcohol as a pathway to other drugs, alcohol dependence and the possibility of long-term health damage (Wright, 1991).

In reviewing the evidence to support or refute such concerns, it is important to separate views about the morality of youthful drinking from objective evidence of alcohol-related harm. We also need to be clear about the nature of these relationships. The existence of an association between a particular harm and the use of alcohol by young people may not necessarily imply a causal relationship. Several studies have observed a clustering of risky drinking behaviour with other risky behaviour in young people such as illicit drug use or anti-social behaviour (Newcombe, Measham and Parker, 1995; Swadi, 1989; Plant and Plant, 1993; Turtle, Jones and Hickman, 1997). Therefore it has been difficult to disentangle the effects of drinking alcohol from other risk factors, and also to separate factors leading to risky drinking behaviour from its outcomes.

BEING YOUNG CARRIES ITS OWN RISKS

The fact that young people are not fully developed, both physically and psychologically, means that they face greater risks in using alcohol.

On a physiological basis, novice drinkers of both sexes will experience greater intoxication (for a given amount of alcohol) than regular drinkers, because they will have acquired little physical tolerance to the drug. Young people who weigh less than adults will also achieve a higher blood-alcohol level.

Children's and adolescents' metabolism of alcohol and their physiological response to intoxication differs from that of adults (Pikkarainen and Raiha, 1969). They develop low levels of blood sugar (hypoglycaemia) more often (Cummins, 1961), and at higher blood-alcohol levels can suffer hypothermia or breathing difficulties (Laminpaa *et al.*, 1993). They are more likely than adults to have a fit as a consequence of drinking and will go into a coma at lower blood-alcohol levels (Royal College of Physicians, 1995). It should not be forgotten that alcohol's depressant effect can more easily produce a fatally toxic overdose in young people and that the amount of alcohol needed for a fatal overdose will be less in younger, lighter, irregular drinkers, especially if they are female.

The increased binge drinking trend among young people is therefore of particular concern in terms of potential health risks. In the early 1980s hospital admissions for alcohol poisoning were calculated at about 1000 per year (Beattie *et al.*, 1986). More than ten years on, these figures are still not collected routinely (Walker, 1997). Robson (1997) reports a ten-fold increase since 1985 in the numbers of young people attending the accident and emergency department of the Royal Liverpool Children's Hospital. In 1985 twenty 11- to 15-year-olds were treated; in the year from February 1996, 200 young people aged 9–16 were treated. They all either needed resuscitation from a large overdose or had injuries from assaults or accidents incurred while they were intoxicated. Most had drunk strong cider or vodka.

As a depressant and disinhibitor, alcohol will exert its impact on the higher faculties of the brain such as judgement and decision-making skills, as well as co-ordination. For example, driving skill is impaired at a lower blood-alcohol concentration in young people than in adults (TRRL, 1993). Young people are still in the process of clarifying their values, discovering their own personal codes of behaviour and learning self-control. As these behaviours are not as well established as in older people, they are more easily affected by alcohol. Young people's lack of experience in how to behave when intoxicated and in handling the effects of alcohol also exposes them to increased risks.

Finally, young people who drink or buy alcohol 'under-age' risk negative interpersonal or social consequences arising from legal and parental sanctions.

ALCOHOL INTOXICATION AND ALCOHOL DEPENDENCE

There is a vast literature on alcohol-related problems. High alcohol consumption is associated with increased rates of illness, affecting almost every organ in the human body (Anderson *et al.*, 1993). No alcohol problem is exclusive to young people, but there is a discernible pattern of alcohol-related problems experienced by younger drinkers. For this group, it is simple intoxication, episodic drunkenness or binge drinking that are most likely to lead to problems such as violence, crime and accidents. Cancers, heart disease, liver cirrhosis and other health consequences of chronic heavy drinking are rarely seen in young drinkers, although physiological differences between the sexes mean that women exhibit permanent organ damage over a shorter drinking career than men. Very few young people die from the direct effects of alcohol. In 1993, 17 people under the age of 25 died from causes directly attributed to alcohol: in 1994 the figure was 12 (NHS Health Advisory Service, 1996). Young people are far more likely to die from the *indirect* effects of alcohol, particularly accidents, suicide and violence (Walker, 1997a). Over twenty years ago, it was calculated that about 500 young people die each year while drunk, representing 10% of all deaths under 25 years of age (Sabey and Coding, 1975). No more recent figure is available (Walker, 1997a).

Studies of the relationship between alcohol consumption and alcohol-related problems in young people show, not surprisingly, that heavier drinkers report more problems. An American survey not only found this broad association but also that specific types of problem were associated with different levels of drinking. Light drinkers experienced physical discomforts such as hangovers and nausea; moderate drinkers showed more school and social problems; heavy drinkers were more likely to get into trouble with the police (Werch, Gorman and Marty, 1987). This suggests a developmental pattern: that when starting to drink, young people have no tolerance and so experience physical effects. As drinking becomes established, then social and legal problems are experienced – though only by a minority of young drinkers.

Youthful drinking behaviour is not a good predictor of alcohol-related illness or physical dependence in later life (Shanks, 1990; Plant, Peck and Samuel, 1995; Sharp and Lowe, 1989). The increased risk of illness requiring a hospital admission observed in heavier drinkers does not appear to apply to those under 35, except for accidents and alcohol-related violence. However, a longitudinal study of Swedish young men born in 1950–51, which related their experience of illness and risk of death before the age of 35 to their drinking habits at age 18, found that those young men who drank more than 250 g of alcohol per week (approximately 30 units) had three times the risk of dying before the age of 35, compared to their peer group as a whole (Andreasson *et al.*, 1990).

The popular image of someone who is dependent on alcohol is someone who is middle-aged, has been drinking heavily for years and cannot stop. Two major British surveys reveal that alcohol dependence and problem drinking are relatively common, particularly among young adults. In comparison to other age groups in England, young adults have high rates of problem drinking and alcohol dependence, although it should be emphasised that problems related to binge episodes of drunkenness are much more common. The OPCS Health Survey for England (OPCS, 1995) defines problem drinkers as those responding 'yes' to at least two of a series of questions designed to assess psychological and physical dependence. It finds that of current drinkers, 9% of men and 5% of women are classified as problem drinkers. The proportion of problem drinkers is highest in the 16–24 (12%) and 23–34 (13%) age groups for men and in the 25–34 age group for women; 6% of 16- to 24-year-old women were problem drinkers. Additionally, 16- to 24-year-olds are more likely to mention symptoms of physical dependence than psychological problems. Predictably young men and women drinking over 50 and 35 units a week respectively are more likely to experience problems associated with physical dependence (OPCS, 1995).

The Psychiatric Morbidity Survey 1993, a major survey on mental health in the United Kingdom, assessed the prevalence of alcohol dependence alongside mental health problems of all kinds (Meltzer, Gill and Pettigrew, 1995). Using a different set of criteria ('yes' answers to at least three of 12 questions about loss of control, symptomatic behaviour and binge drinking)* it finds 47 out of a 1000 people aged 16–24 show signs of dependence on alcohol. For men the figure is about 6.75% and for women about 2.75%. Highest rates for men are in the 20–24 age group, at over 17%, and falling steadily after that. Nearly 12% of 16- to 19-year-old males are classified as alcohol dependent. In women, the highest rates are in the 16- to 19-year-old age group, at about 7% and rates are also high in 20- to 24-year-old women (4%).

Both of these surveys only included people living in private households, excluding those in institutions or who are homeless. Prevalence rates of problem drinking and alcohol dependence among these groups are much higher.

Walker (1997b) points out that for young teenagers, there is no reliable evidence about alcohol dependence to fill the gap between anecdotal and often sensationalist coverage in the media and incomplete official data.

---

* Binge drinking was defined as staying drunk for several days at a time.

In 1994–95, 50 children aged 10–14 and 129 aged 15–19 were treated in hospital for 'alcohol dependence syndrome' (Department of Health, 1996). These statistics may overlap with the emergency admissions reported above.

Very few alcohol treatment services offer any specialist help to young people. This is a limitation common to substance misuse services in general. The NHS Health Advisory Service report (1996) on substance misuse services in England and Wales, which included alcohol and drug services found that there is a lack of recognition by purchasers and providers of health services of needs arising from substance misuse by young people. Services are extremely limited in availability and scope, where services exist at all, and they have developed in a patchy and idiosyncratic manner. Responses have been poorly planned and co-ordinated. Much of the limited existing service is provided by voluntary agencies in the non-statutory sector.

THE IMMEDIATE NEGATIVE CONSEQUENCES OF DRINKING

Drinking alcohol is a positive experience for most young people. There is little doubt that drinking alcohol is associated by young people with social enjoyment, just as it is with adults. When asked to describe their experience of drinking in terms of a range of consequences, the majority, from the age of 13 upwards, report emotional and social benefits such as feeling happy, having a good time and feeling at ease with friends (Hawker, 1978; Marsh, Dobbs and White, 1986; Newcombe, Measham and Parker, 1995). As they grow older and their expertise in drinking increases, they report positive experiences more frequently.

In learning drinking skills, adolescents go through the same learning curve as applies to the development of any other new skill (Wright, 1993). They make mistakes and try different strategies, with novices facing the greatest likelihood of harm. For example, frequency of reporting having experienced at least one of the immediate acute negative effects of drinking peaks at 15 for both sexes, with young women reporting as many negative consequences as young men at this age.

The commonest negative consequence is a hangover, which will have been experienced by about half of England's young people by the time they are 15. Other common experiences, reported by between a third and half of young people by the time they are 15, are physiological responses to the drug alcohol, for example being unable to remember parts of the night before, being sick, feeling dizzy or faint, or falling over (Hawker, 1978; Marsh, Dobbs and White, 1986; Newcombe, Measham and Parker, 1995).

Young adults aged 16–24 experience more negative personal effects of drinking than other adult age groups (Goddard, 1998), in line with their higher levels of drinking and frequency of getting drunk (Table 10). They are also much more likely to have witnessed a fight after people have been drinking. The 1997 ONS English national survey found that 68% of all 16- to 24-year-olds sampled (including non-drinkers) had witnessed a fight in the last year, compared with 29% of all adults.

Table 10 Experience of the personal effects of drinking

	16–24 years	All adults
Injured by an accident after drinking (%)	7	2
Said something regretted after drinking (%)	30	12
Had argument after drinking (%)	34	16

(Base: all those who had an alcoholic drink in the last year)
Source: Goddard (1998)

There are significant gender differences in the type of negative consequences of drinking reported by young people aged under 18. Young women are more likely to report emotional experiences and negative social consequences, for example feeling unhappy, being afraid to go home or having an argument. In contrast, young men are more likely to report drink-related involvement in criminal activities, for example vandalism, theft and driving a car or motorbike (Hawker, 1978; Newcombe, Measham and Parker, 1995).

After the age of 16, as males' and females' drinking patterns diverge, young women report fewer adverse consequences, in line with their lower consumption levels (Goddard, 1998). The national survey by Marsh, Dobbs and White (1986) found that nearly half of 17-year-old young men had been sick after drinking compared with only 13% of young women aged 17. In this age group, a third of males had felt dizzy, confused or had a headache, and 29% had fallen over after drinking, while the corresponding figures for young women were 11% and 7%.

Interestingly, Marsh, Dobbs and White's study found that both positive and negative experiences of drinking were correlated with being drunk. The greater the degree of social enjoyment the adolescents recalled as being associated with an evening's drinking, the more likely it was to be followed by unpleasant physical consequences, such as being sick, feeling ill, or by behaviour which was later regretted.

This finding can be understood in terms of young people's motivations for drinking. Those who deliberately seek the buzz of intoxication, readily acknowledge the possibility of negative consequences (Coffield and Gofton, 1994; Mathrani, 1998) although an Australian study suggests that they are likely to understand the likelihood of the more serious consequences of binge drinking (Gillespie *et al.*, 1991).

ACCIDENTS AND INJURY

In terms of physical health risks, accidents are the most important serious negative consequence of young people's drinking (NHS Health Advisory Service, 1996). Accidents and violence account for more deaths during adolescence than any other cause (Shanks, 1990). In a review of the English language literature, Hingson and Howland (1993) established that, across the whole age range, up to 50% of head injuries, 13–37% of non-fatal falls, 21–47% of drownings and 9–68% of burn deaths are alcohol related, as are 35% of accidents at work, 14% of all road accident deaths and 30% of accidents involving pedestrians. They estimate alcohol to be a factor in 20–30% of all accidents.

A UK national survey of facial injuries conducted in 1997 found alcohol was a factor in 22% of all facial injuries, 43% of serious facial injuries and 45% of facial fractures. Alcohol was most commonly implicated in facial injuries experienced by young people aged 15–25. There were estimated to be 50,000 assaults involving facial injuries to 15- to 25-year-olds and 61% of these were alcohol related. Almost all assaults with bottles or glasses (98%) were alcohol related and half of these incidents took place in bars (Hutchison *et al.*, 1998).

Accidents, particularly on the roads (as drivers, passengers or pedestrians) and near water, are especially common in the under-25s (Alcohol Concern, 1991; Niblett, 1995). In 1993, nearly half of car driver fatalities who had been over the legal blood alcohol limit were in their twenties or younger. One-fifth were aged 16–19 (Hayden, 1995). Male drivers in their twenties are the group most likely to fail a breath test or be involved in a drink-driving accident (Alcohol Concern, 1997c). Drivers aged under 20 have more accidents than older drivers, even at blood alcohol levels below the legal limit (Denney, 1986), confirming that inexperience in driving and inexperience in drinking are a particularly risky combination.

Car drivers represent less than half the casualties in drink-related car accidents; passengers are as likely as drivers to be killed or seriously injured. In 1995, casualties included over 700 pedestrians and nearly 200 cyclists. Though women are much less likely to drink themselves, almost a third of those killed or injured are women and nearly 5% are children. About three-quarters of pedestrians killed between 10.00 p.m. and 4.00 a.m. were over the legal limit for driving (Denney, 1997).

From 1987 to 1991 there was a dramatic increase in alcohol-related home and leisure accidents, although these were not broken down by age (Alcohol Concern, 1994).

The government's strategy document *Our Healthier Nation* (Department of Health, 1998) highlights alcohol as a significant factor in accidents; particularly to young people aged 15–24. Fatal accidents among young men, accidents involving pedestrians and those to young children in the charge of intoxicated adults were identified as especially important in *The Health of the Nation* (Department of Health, 1992). For example a Scottish study by Squires and Busuttil (1995) found alcohol to be involved in about 30% of child deaths in house fires.

ALCOHOL AND CRIME

Common sense might suggest that young people getting involved in crime as a result of drinking alcohol is a serious and legitimate cause for public concern. Parker observes that one of the central tenets of current political discourse on law and order 'requires youth, alcohol and offending to be inseparably handcuffed' (Parker, 1996, p. 282). However, unravelling cause and effect in the relationship between young people's drinking and crime is not as straightforward as it seems. While alcohol is *associated* with a wide range of crimes, it is not necessarily the *cause* of crime.

In addition to crimes that are alcohol-defined, for example drink-driving offences, there is certainly ample evidence of an *association* between alcohol and a whole range of crimes. Recorded offences of drunkenness in England and Wales rose steadily throughout the 1970s and 1980s to a peak of 93,000 in 1989. Since then, the number of drunkenness offences has steadily decreased to 42,500 in 1995. This decrease is more likely to be due to changes in police priorities than a reduction in drunkenness (Home Office, 1996a). The rate of convictions for drunkenness peaks at age 18 for both sexes; this age group is almost twice as likely to be charged or cautioned for drunkenness as 21- to 29-year-olds. Almost half of the incidents of disorderly behaviour occur after pub closing time, particularly at weekends. Police estimate that 20–30% of violent incidents take place in or near licensed premises. It should be noted that although under-age drinking is the norm, the number of convictions does not reflect this: in England and Wales in 1995, only 351 persons under 18 were found guilty or cautioned for buying alcohol and 161 licensees cautioned for selling alcohol to under-18s (Home Office, 1996a).

Much of the recent interest in alcohol and offending has focused on violent crime. In the British Crime Survey 1986, 50% of victims of wounding said the offender 'had been drinking', as did 44% of victims of assault and 30% of victims of sexual offences (Home Office Standing Conference on Prevention, 1987). According to the 1996 Crime Survey, four out of ten violent crimes involve alcohol. This includes 53% of violence by strangers, 45% of violence by acquaintances, 32% of domestic violence and 17% of muggings (Home Office, 1996b). In Bristol, an accident and emergency department study of 18- to 35-year-old males injured in urban city centre violence found that at least 85% of assaults took place in a bar or shortly after leaving one (Shepherd and Brinkley, 1996). Modest drinking was not associated with increased risk of injury in assaults, but binge drinking (defined as consuming more than 10 units of alcohol), especially at weekends, was found to be an important risk factor.

Young adults (17–24) are known to be the heaviest drinkers in the population and are also the most likely age group to be involved in crime. Offending is not unusual among young people. If undetected, minor crimes are included, it has been estimated that over 80% of adolescents become involved in crime of some kind, although only a minority are detected and even fewer commit serious offences (Farrington, 1987). By far the commonest crime for juveniles (10–17) is theft (nearly 60% of all offences). Criminal activity has always been a largely male behaviour, with less than 20% of offenders being female. The peak age for known offending is lower in women: 15 years, compared to 18 in men. There is a tendency for most young people to grow out of both types of behaviour, risky drinking and offending, as they reach their mid-20s (NACRO, 1997).

A longitudinal study in the North West of England (Newcombe, Measham and Parker, 1995) is following a cohort of 14- to 15-year-olds over three years, to investigate the relationship between adolescence, drinking and deviance. Young people were asked about their involvement in 14 different deviant and criminal acts of varying degrees of severity, ranging from making a noise at night, to burglary and car theft. The list also included adult-oriented behaviours, such as driving a car and going to a night club, which, were clearly status offences because of the age of the respondents.

Results from the first year identify a significant and strong correlation between deviance and the frequency and amount of alcohol consumed by the study group. Deviance, in some degree, was so common as to be normal within the age group, with 80% of respondents admitting to at least one deviant act in the last year. These acts were commonly making a noise at night, threatening someone or going to a nightclub. Frequent drinkers, heavier drinkers and 'bar' drinkers were far more likely to have been deviant, stopped by the police, arrested and convicted. This study also noted that those young people who did not drink alcohol were primarily from Muslim families. This group reported low rates of deviance.

McMurran (1992) has pointed out that there are eleven ways in which alcohol and crime may be related (Figure 12).

---

1. DRINKING IS THE CRIME (for example under-age drinking; drunk and disorderly; drinking and driving)

2. DRINKING CHANGES BEHAVIOUR (for example disinhibition; impairment of judgement; giving courage)

3. DRINKING CAUSES PROBLEMS WHICH THEN LEAD TO CRIME (for example overspending; losing jobs; arguments with friends or family)

4. THE DRINKING CONTEXT LEAD TO CRIME (for example committing crimes in pubs or clubs; meeting friends in pubs or clubs and planning crimes with them)

5. CRIME SUPPORTS DRINKING (for example stealing alcohol; or stealing money to buy alcohol)

6. UNDERLYING PROBLEMS LEAD TO DRINKING AND TO CRIME (for example unhappy home situation leads to staying out either drinking or getting into trouble)

7. DRINKING OCCURS AFTER CRIME (for example to celebrate or to cope with guilt)

8. DRINKING IS AN EXCUSE FOR CRIME (mitigation)

9. DRINKING INCREASES CHANCES OF ARREST (for example through carelessness)

10. DRINKING REDUCES CRIME (for example through incapacitation)

11. DRINKING AND CRIME ARE NOT RELATED

Source: McMurran (1992)

Figure 12 Relationships between alcohol and crime

There is an enormous international research literature on the relationship between alcohol and crime. Recent British studies have confirmed the complexity of attributing cause and effect (Tuck, 1989; Marsh and Fox Kibby, 1992; Parker, 1996). Reducing McMurran's analysis to three principal relationships – drinking causes crime, crime causes drinking, and drinking and crime share common causes – there is evidence to support all three relationships (Fergusson, Lynskey and Horwood, 1996). Laboratory experiments show that anti-social behaviour, particularly aggression, increases with increased doses of alcohol. There are many studies that find that heavy drinking by young people and offending behaviour have shared antecedents, including family life, use of other drugs, intelligence and early behavioural tendencies. There is also evidence that anti-social behaviour may lead to alcohol misuse. Sumner and Parker (1995), in a review of the literature on alcohol and crime, note that certain types of explanations of the alcohol–crime relationship seem to have been attached to particular types of crime. For example, the use of alcohol as an excuse has been examined in relation to rape and wife beating, whereas the effects of alcohol on cognition have mainly been discussed with regard to murder and non-domestic violence; the drinking environment has only been viewed as relevant to public disorder crimes.

On balance, recent longitudinal studies have found that young people's drinking and offending share common causes rather than drinking causes crime (Fergusson, Lynskey and Horwood, 1996; Raskin White, Hansell and Brick, 1993). Even in drink-defined offences such as drink driving and drunkenness, early social, family and behavioural factors and use of other drugs have been identified as contributing to these crimes, in addition to drinking alcohol (Karlsson and Romelsjö, 1997). In New Zealand, data gathered during a 16-year longitudinal study was used to examine the linkages between alcohol misuse and juvenile offending in 15- to 16-year-olds (Fergusson, Lynskey and Horwood, 1996). The results confirmed previous studies in finding that 16-year-olds of both sexes who drank heavily, frequently or problematically were at increased risk of committing both violent and property crimes. To a large extent, these associations were found to be derived from risk factors shared by both alcohol misuse and juvenile offending. The shared risk factors were intelligence, parental substance use, conduct problems in middle childhood, juvenile offending by age 15 and affiliations with delinquent peers. Taking these risk factors into account, there was no association between alcohol misuse and property crimes. There was a direct cause-and-effect association between alcohol misuse and violent crimes, in addition to the effects of the common antecedents.

As Fergusson, Lynskey and Horwood (1996) point out, these statistical findings based on populations do not preclude the possibility of other relationships between alcohol and crime at the individual level, such as those identified by McMurran. This is borne out by the results of studies of young offenders. Several surveys of young offenders have found that a high proportion are heavy drinkers or dependent on alcohol and that the relationships between alcohol consumption and criminal behaviour are complex. One study found that most young offenders thought that drinking had led them to do things they would not do if they were sober, but the researchers point out that this could be a convenient excuse for not taking responsibility for their actions. The social context was frequently cited: meeting and drinking with friends, which set off a train of events culminating in a crime. Others said they drank after the crime to relieve guilt or celebrate (McMurran and Hollin, 1993). A study contrasting quantifiable data and motivational accounts obtained from in-depth interviews with persistent young adult offenders, most of whom were also heavy drinkers, also showed that drinking careers and criminal careers overlapped in complex ways (Parker, 1996). This study highlighted the inadequacies of isolating alcohol as the key variable, without also examining other drug use. Respondents interchanged alcohol and illegal drugs and used different drugs for different purposes at different times. For example, one young car thief described how he used amphetamine to keep alert for car taking at night, tranquillisers for daytime sleeping and alcohol to get drunk on the proceeds of his criminal activity.

As Alcohol Concern point out (Alcohol Concern, 1996b), whatever the connections between alcohol use by young people and crime, it is important to remember that:

- most young people over 16 drink alcohol and do not commit criminal offences

- alcohol-using offenders do not commit crimes every time they drink.

ALCOHOL, AGGRESSION AND VIOLENCE

Researchers generally agree that aggressive behaviour and alcohol use are related. Young people, especially young males, are more likely to drink heavily and more likely to be involved in aggression and violence, both as victims and perpetrators (Home Office, 1996a; Coggans and McKellar, 1995). Among under-18s, boys are more likely than girls to become involved in fights, vandalism and to attract the attention of the police (Parker and Measham, 1994). A study of accident and emergency service usage has found that people injured in cases of assault are more likely to have been drinking at the time than those injured in other ways (Hayden, 1995) while people who have been assaulted are likely themselves to be occasionally 'heavy' or 'binge' drinkers (Yates, 1987).

There is ample evidence to indicate that alcohol is implicated in violent crimes (see discussion above). As with relationships between alcohol and crime, the relationship between alcohol and aggression could be of three types:

Alcohol causes aggressive behaviour mainly through chemical effects on the brain such as disinhibition, bad judgement.

Aggressive behaviour leads to heavy drinking, assuming that those people who are inherently aggressive drink more alcohol, either because they belong to heavy drinking sub-cultures or because they use alcohol to relax or as an excuse to act aggressively.

Alcohol and aggression are related because they share a common cause – some other factor or factors link the two behaviours.

A recent American study (Raskin White, Hansell and Brick, 1993) both reviewed the evidence to support each of these hypotheses in relation to adolescents and examined data from a prospective longitudinal study of adolescent development. Taken as a whole, while there was evidence to support all three types of relationship, their findings supported the second hypothesis most strongly, suggesting that aggressive behaviour among adolescents is developed at an early age and sets the stage for later alcohol use and alcohol-related aggression, especially for males. In support of the third hypothesis, they also note that both drinking and aggression have shared antecedents, such as family pathology and child abuse, which may account for the clustering of social risk factors among adolescents.

Coggans and McKellar (1995) reached similar conclusions in examining the evidence related to alcohol and aggression in adolescents in Britain. They note similar shared antecedents, such as early social influences and family discord. They also argue that 'alcohol-related violence may have less to do with alcohol *per se* than with the social context in which people drink, particularly people with aggressive tendencies.' (p. 61)

ALCOHOL AND YOUNG PEOPLE'S MENTAL HEALTH

Many young people suffering from severe psychiatric disorders are also diagnosed as having serious substance misuse problems, including alcohol misuse. The most common mental illnesses co-diagnosed alongside substance misuse are anxiety disorders, affective disorders and anti-social personality (NHS Health Advisory Service, 1996). There is a positive association between alcohol use and depression in young people (Deykin, Buka and Zeena, 1992) and with suicide and attempted suicide in male adolescents (Hawton *et al.*, 1993). There is also a positive association between 'episodes of alcohol intoxication' and eating disorders (Lavik, Clausen and Pedersen, 1991).

As with the other risks and harms associated with young people's drinking, discovering whether drinking alcohol causes mental health problems or vice versa is difficult to ascertain from the research evidence. Much of the research is from North America, where the social norms and cultural mores surrounding youthful drinking are considerably less tolerant than those in the UK. Consequently, young people defined as problem drinkers, or deviant in other ways, in the USA, might not be defined in the same way in the UK. Longitudinal studies on alcohol and mental illness, which would help to define the direction of causation, are generally lacking.

ALCOHOL AND SEXUAL RISK-TAKING

Most young people drink and many young people are sexually active. It is popularly believed that young people, especially young women, will have sex more readily and will take more sexual risks when under the influence of alcohol than when they are sober. In research terms, how alcohol affects sexual behaviour and whether alcohol use *causes* sexual risk-taking has yet to be established. It is often difficult to establish whether a study is demonstrating the uninhibiting effect of alcohol on sexual encounters, or whether people who drink are simply more likely to take risks (HEA, 1997). Recent reviews of the literature have concluded that the growing numbers of studies in the last decade have produced conflicting results (Plant and Plant, 1993; Donovan and McEwan, 1995), at least for HIV-related risk-taking. Donovan and McEwan experienced similar difficulties to those faced by this reviewer, in attempting to make comparisons across different sample populations. They point out that there are enormous cultural differences in alcohol use across different countries and, within countries, in different groups of people. Cultural differences are rarely commented on in such studies. They also found that definitions of risky sex were so variable that they made cross-study comparison impossible, and few studies have taken into account the context in which sexual behaviour takes place. The influence of alcohol on sexual behaviour may vary according to the group of people concerned, so that extrapolations from heterosexuals to homosexuals may be inappropriate (Donovan and McEwan, 1995). Studies by Leigh (1990a, 1990b), Gold and Skinner (1992) and Gold, Karmiloff-Smith and Skinner (1992) indicate that lesbians, homosexual men and young heterosexual people combine alcohol with sexual activity in different ways, reflecting the different sub-cultures of these groups.

In the UK, studies of white heterosexual populations suggest a positive association between drinking alcohol before sexual activity and not using contraception (Robertson and Plant, 1988; McEwan *et al.*,1991). Most studies have found no association between alcohol use and risky sex in homosexual male populations (HEA, 1997).

There is considerable evidence that young people *combine* alcohol and sex, especially immediately prior to their first sexual experience (Flannigan, McLean and Propp, 1990; Plant, 1990; Klein and Pitman,

1993). Young people are also more likely than older people to say that emotions influence their drinking and are more likely to drink when experiencing positive emotions, especially romance and stimulation (Klein and Pitman, 1993).

Donovan and McEwan (1995) point out that drinking alcohol and sexual interaction are both extremely common aspects of young people's social behaviour. Both sexual arousal and alcohol are powerful disinhibitors. The part played by alcohol in sexual risk-taking is bound up in the social rituals, expectancies and meanings placed on drinking and on sex by groups of young people and on the 'social worlds' in which these interactions take place. For example, a qualitative study by Hirst (1994) of the social and sexual lives of 15- to 16-year-olds in Sheffield found that for the majority of those interviewed, socialising involved sex and drinking alcohol. Most sexual activity occurred under the influence of alcohol for white males and females (but not for the sexual activities of Pakistani or Somali teenagers, who did not drink). For white teenagers, alcohol was considered to be influential in affecting the outcomes of an evening's sexual activity and was also very prominent in their explanations and justifications for sexual behaviour. The main factors, in order of importance, in determining how far young women would go sexually were:

1. Level of alcohol consumption

2. Amount of time available

3. Attractiveness of a potential partner, as judged by self or friends

4. Privacy.

Similarly the main obstacles to 'going all the way' (vaginal penetration) for young men were:

1. Being too drunk

2. Restrictions on time

3. Willingness of partner.

The young people involved in this study were aware that their drinking and sexual risk-taking were related. They believed that drinking alcohol reduced their chances of using a condom, and none believed that alcohol would increase their confidence in negotiating safer sex. While alcohol clearly played an important part in sexual risk-taking for this group of young people, it cannot be concluded that their drinking *caused* unsafe sex. Hirst suggests that their constant references to alcohol as explanations for behaviour could equally be interpreted as indirect excuses for denying any personal responsibility for their actions.

A small-scale, qualitative and quantitative study by Scott (1992) of 18- to 25-year-olds in Allinton NHS Trust, England asked them to recall specific experiences of risky sex. None mentioned alcohol spontaneously and risky sex occurred with or without alcohol. Alcohol was not perceived a causing risky sex, but as a social rather than sexual disinhibitor. This study and others in England conducted with students (McEwan *et al.*, 1991; Gold, Karmiloff-Smith and Skinner, 1992) have found that, in student's reports and explanations of specific risky sexual experiences, drinking alcohol is particularly important in casual sexual encounters. The students perceived that because of drinking, they were likely to become more sexually involved with someone than they would normally want and that they would be less likely to use contraception. The study by Gold and colleagues found that students with casual partners were more intoxicated than those in a relationship at all points in the 'evening' and that they were more confident that they could perceive whether a new partner was likely to be HIV-infected. Scott's study found that young adults in relationships avoided alcohol with sex because they felt it decreased pleasure and they perceived no need for social disinhibition.

A Norwegian study of Norwegian 16- to 20-year-olds explored the association between drinking and failure to use contraceptives (Traeen and Kvalem, 1996). For both sexes, those who drank alcohol before sex were more likely than non-drinkers to attribute reasons for engaging in sexual intercourse to external, situational factors (partner wanted it, it just happened) than to internal factors (love, arousal, curiosity, excitement). The authors interpret the relationship between alcohol and sex in terms of the Nordic, socially accepted 'sexual script' – how sexual behaviour is guided and controlled by means of group and context-specific norms and rules (Gagnon and Simon, 1977). They propose that the function of alcohol in sexual scripts is to overcome the social rules that would otherwise limit sexual behaviour:

> 'Drinking and/or intoxication may be of importance for feeling "swept away" and being "swept away" may allow for a kind of "time out" where the probability of engaging in unprotected sexual intercourse increases.' (Traeen and Kvalem, 1996, p. 1004)

These studies illustrate the complexity of the relationship between young people's drinking and their sexual behaviour. They demonstrate the functional nature of drinking by young people, with the conscious use of alcohol as a social disinhibitor, to help in making new sexual relationships. They also demonstrate the importance of young people's expectations of alcohol's effects as influences on their sexual behaviour.

ALCOHOL AND OTHER DRUG USE

There is a significant positive correlation between alcohol use and misuse by young people and their use of tobacco and illicit drugs. Alcohol and tobacco are commonly regarded as 'gateway' drugs. Drug-users begin their experience of mind-altering substances through the use of tobacco and alcohol, a proportion move on to use 'soft drugs' such as cannabis, LSD or ecstasy and a small minority progress to 'hard' drugs such as heroin or cocaine. These 'stages of drug use' as proposed by Kandel (1978), have some empirical support from American longitudinal studies of drug use and life history accounts of drug misusers. However, use of the term 'gateway' should be interpreted as a presentation of possibilities, rather than an automatic route that all young drinkers follow, especially given the near universality of adolescent drinking in the United Kingdom. Not all adolescents who experience a particular stage will go on to a later stage. Furthermore, just as patterns of drug use show considerable geographical and cultural variation, there is some evidence that the pathways to illicit drug use may also vary. For example, a longitudinal study of stages in adolescent drug use in Norway (Aas and Pedersen, 1993), found that the path to use of illicit drugs (other than cannabis) was more common when inhalants (for example glue and solvents) are used between the use of legal drugs (alcohol and tobacco) and cannabis. A recent American study of serious drug-users found that while drinking usually precedes 'soft' drug use, previous cannabis use is a more common path to serious drug use (Golub and Johnson, 1994).

Drug-use pathways among young people in Britain are likely to be changing because patterns of consumption have altered dramatically in the last 10 to 15 years. Recreational consumption of illicit substances is becoming increasingly normalised within youth culture. More young people are using illicit drugs and they are using a wider range of drugs. Among schoolchildren, around one in twelve 12-year-olds and one in three 14-year-olds have tried illegal drugs (ISDD, 1997). Two-thirds of 15- to 16-year-olds in England have been offered an illegal drug, and four out of ten have tried an illegal drug, most commonly cannabis (Turtle, Jones and Hickman, 1997). Half of all 16- to 25-year-olds say they have used drugs (ISDD, 1997). Smoking is declining among adults but continuing to increase among young teenagers, with girls being more likely than boys to be smokers.

Young teenagers who are frequent drinkers are much more likely to be regular smokers. This applies to all ages from 11–16 and to both sexes (Lader and Matheson, 1991; HEA/Mori, 1992b; Goddard, 1997a). In England in 1996, among 11- to 16-year-olds, only 8% of regular smokers say they never drink. In contrast, nearly two-thirds (61%) of those who don't smoke are also non-drinkers. Most non-drinkers have never experimented with cigarettes. Nearly half the regular smokers in this age group also drink at least once a week, and nearly a third of regular drinkers smoke regularly (Goddard, 1997a).

Plant, Peck and Samuel (1985) examined the smoking, drinking and drug-using habit of school leavers (16- to 17-year-olds) in the Lothian Region of Scotland and followed them up three years later when they were aged 19–20. At both initial interview and follow-up, among both sexes, the level of alcohol consumption, the number of negative alcohol-related consequences experienced and the number of serious alcohol-related consequences were significantly and positively correlated with the number of cigarettes smoked daily, the number of illicit drugs ever used and the number of category A drugs ever used (category A drugs are those which carry the most severe legal penalties for possession and supply, for example heroin, cocaine, ecstasy). In both sexes, use of illicit drugs was

135

more strongly associated with alcohol use, and experience of negative alcohol-related consequences, than was cigarette smoking.

An HEA survey of 9- to 15-year-olds in England conducted in 1989 (HEA/MORI, 1992b) and the HBSC survey of 11- to 16-year-olds conducted in 1995 (Turtle, Jones and Hickman, 1996) reveal similar patterns in relation to alcohol consumption and use of other drugs to those found for older teenagers. The first survey found that few (6%) non-drinkers had been offered drugs and just 2% had ever tried them. A far higher proportion of drinkers had been offered or tried drugs. A quarter of occasional drinkers and a third of regular drinkers had been offered drugs. Six years later, among 15- to 16-year-olds, the HBSC survey reveals the same associations between smoking, drinking and drug use, against a background of increased experience of drugs. Although drinkers continue to be much more likely than non-drinkers to be offered drugs (76% compared to 40%), these percentages indicate that drug offers are still relatively commonplace, even for non-drinkers. There is considerably more difference between drinkers and non-drinkers in relation to drug *use*; half of the drinkers had tried an illicit substance, compared with 17% of non-drinkers, and drug-users were twice as likely as non-users to have been 'really drunk' ten or more times (Turtle, Jones and Hickman, 1996).

A longitudinal study in the North West of England of young people's drinking and deviant behaviour is following a cohort of 14- to 15-year-old school pupils over four years (Measham, Newcombe and Parker, 1994). The researchers have noted that alcohol use is an important 'pathway' to drug use. In their sample, drinkers are far more likely to have been in situations where drugs were on offer and to have experienced offers of drugs than those who drink less frequently. This trend continues with actual drug use. Over half of the weekly drinkers have tried a drug in the last year compared with only 1 in 15 non-drinkers; 4 in 10 have used a drug in the last month compared with 1 in 25 non-drinkers (Parker and Measham, 1994).

Other local surveys of prevalence of alcohol and drug use among school-age adolescents in Southern England (Diamond *et al.*, 1988) and in Nottingham (Bean *et al.*, 1988) have reached the same conclusion about the shared social settings for drinking and illicit drug use. Using pubs, clubs and discos brings young drinkers into environments where illegal drugs are available.

The association between heavy or frequent drinking, illicit drug use and smoking has also been interpreted as support for Jessor's Problem Behaviour theory (Jessor and Jessor, 1977). This is discussed further under 'Theories derived from analytical studies' in Chapter 7.

Rational, economic arguments have also been advanced. On the basis of qualitative research with young people aged 12–24 in the North East of England, Coffield and Gofton (1994) argue that young people evaluate 'soft' drugs (LSD, cannabis, poppers, ecstasy, speed) as 'more bangs per buck' than either alcohol or tobacco. They suggest that soft drugs provide young users with many of the same satisfactions as alcohol or tobacco but that they are thought to be better value for money, have fewer harmful after-effects and are easier to control.

'Cannabis, evaluated as a product in terms of safety and relative price, is competing successfully with alcohol and tobacco. It is perceived to be relatively cheap, safe, and sociable, in that it can be shared in a "round" like cigarettes or beer. Although alcohol remains the most popular drug overall, it is thought to be comparatively expensive.'
(Coffield and Gofton, 1994, p. 21)

7. Understanding young people's drinking

SUMMARY

1. In contrast to the considerable descriptive data on young people's drinking, much less is known about *why* British young people drink, the place and meaning of drinking alcohol in young people's lives, the social contexts for drinking and the value attached to alcohol use.

2. Analytical studies have examined three major groups of factors and how they relate to young people's drinking behaviour, especially heavy or risky drinking and alcohol-related risks and harms. The three groups of factors are demographic variables, intrapersonal factors, and inter-personal factors and social/environmental influences. There have also been a lesser number of studies attempting to determine how important different factors are in influencing a particular behaviour or consequence of drinking.

3. British analytical studies of young people's drinking are relatively rare and a large proportion of work is derived from North American studies. Cultural differences between young drinkers in the UK and the USA, particularly North American classifications of young heavy drinkers or young problem drinkers, mean that the results of North American analytical studies must be treated with caution.

4. Four theoretical models predominate in analytical studies of young drinkers. These are:

   • problem behaviour theory

   • social learning theory

   • reasoned action/planned behaviour theory

   • social/environmental influences.

5. There is some evidence to support each of these theories. The lack of British analytical studies means that there is insufficient direct evidence to support any one theory in preference to another, or to enable a convincing synthesis of several differing perspectives to be prepared.

6. Interpretations derived from the relatively few qualitative and ethnographic studies support the view that the social contexts for young people's drinking are an important key to understanding alcohol's place and meaning. As young people's social worlds are diverse and local, care must be taken in extrapolating conclusions from these studies to young people in general.

7. Key themes emerging from these studies are:

    - The functional nature of drinking

    - The importance of the buzz

    - The importance of the drinking group, settings and local networks

    - Drinking as hedonism

    - Drinking as time out

    - Drinking as consumerism

    - Drinking as part of leisure

    - Drinking combined with illicit drug use

    - The importance of boundaries in young people's lives.

    *

This review has established that in England, drinking alcohol is normal adolescent behaviour, and that by the age of 18 non-drinkers are rare, except within ethnic and religious groups that prohibit or disapprove of alcohol use. As May (1992) has pointed out, we now have a considerable amount of descriptive data which defines what, where and when young people drink alcohol.

Much less is known about *why* British young people drink, the place and meaning of drinking alcohol in young people's lives, the social contexts for drinking and the value attached to alcohol use. This chapter brings together some of the interpretations reported in the previous chapters to consider briefly theories which seek to explain young people's drinking.

ANALYTICAL STUDIES

Analytical studies attempting to explain young people's drinking, have examined three major groups of factors and how they relate to drinking behaviour, especially heavy or risky drinking and alcohol-related risks and harms. There has also been a lesser number of studies attempting to determine how important different factors are in influencing a particular behaviour or consequence of drinking.

The three groups of factors are:

1. *Demographic variables*, for example sex, age, socio-economic status, income, geographical area or living arrangements.

2. *Intrapersonal factors*, i.e. factors relating to the individual drinker. These include both personality variables and cognitive structures such as expectancies, motivations and attitude schema.

3. *Inter-personal factors, cultural and social/environmental influences*, such as specific settings for drinking, social norms, peer relationships and family dynamics.

Sharp and Lowe (1989) have observed that many of the analytical studies have used frameworks which seek to define young people's drinking as pathological in some way, by examining personality traits, peer group pressure and relationships with other problem behaviours such as family dysfunction or delinquency. They point out that this runs the risk of turning what is essentially a normal part of adolescent socialisation into something deviant:

'It is highly unlikely that over 90 per cent of the 16-year-old population are victims of poor parents, pressuring peers and inadequate personalities. The way forward seems to lie in understanding what drinking means to a young person and how these meanings are propagated.'   (Sharp and Lowe, 1989)

140

THEORIES DERIVED FROM ANALYTICAL STUDIES

While the majority of young people in England drink alcohol, only a minority experience problems related to their drinking. A wide range of theories have been developed, with varying degrees of empirical support, to try to explain why some young people experience alcohol-related harm and others do not. British analytical studies of young people's drinking are relatively rare and a large proportion of work is derived from North American studies. For reasons discussed earlier, the large cultural differences that exist between young drinkers in the UK and the USA, mean that the results of North American studies must be treated with caution. In particular, North American classifications of young heavy drinkers or young problem drinkers may not be appropriate to young people in Britain, and the legal position is different – under-age drinking in any setting is illegal in the USA.

Four theoretical models predominate in analytical studies of young drinkers. These are:

• problem behaviour theory

• social learning theory

• reasoned action/planned behaviour theory

• social/environmental influences.

Each of these theories will be briefly explained and the evidence to support it presented. However, it should be noted that the lack of British analytical studies means that there is insufficient direct evidence to support any one theory in preference to another, or to enable a convincing synthesis of several differing perspectives to be prepared.

Observations that several types of risky or anti-social behaviour are inter-related have informed Jessor's *problem behaviour theory* (Jessor and Jessor, 1977). This is an individually based, psychological perspective which argues that certain individuals are predisposed to adopt a range of problem behaviours, such as heavy drinking, because they have particular personalities and beliefs and behave in ways which are approved of by others who are important to them.

On the basis of longitudinal studies in the USA, Jessor and colleagues have reported that adolescent problem behaviours are interrelated (Jessor, Chase and Donovan, 1980; Donovan and Jessor, 1978; Jessor, Donovan and Costa, 1991). Similar clusters of problem behaviours have been observed in Sweden, where a longitudinal study found that early social and behavioural factors, substance misuse and risky use of alcohol were all predictors for both drunken driving and public drunkenness (Karlsson and Romelsjö, 1997). Jessor's argument, which in the UK is supported by Plant and Plant (1992) and by the HEA's HBSC data (Turtle, Jones and Hickman, 1997), is that there are organised patterns of adolescent risk-taking behaviours and that such risk-taking is part of adolescent lifestyles.

Within the British context, problem behaviour theory has been criticised because it implies that young people's drinking is deviant (Sharp and Lowe, 1989). It also fails to take into account the influence that the drinking environment has on young people's drinking (Knibbe, Oostveen and Van de Goor, 1991) . However, in terms of interventions, the evidence that heavy drinking is correlated with other risky behaviour such as illicit drug use or unsafe sexual practices, implies a need for health promotion initiatives which adopt a broad lifestyle approach, rather than focusing solely on drinking behaviour.

Social learning theory proposes that drinking alcohol is learned behaviour. According to Maloff *et al.* (1979) children learn 'cultural recipes' which explain how to use alcohol (and other substances) to obtain desired results. Cultural recipes also describe where, when, how much and what type of alcohol consumption is socially sanctioned. Children and young people learn these recipes through the *modelling* and *reinforcement* of people who are significant to them, especially family and peers (Bandura, 1977).

A considerable body of empirical evidence supports this theory, as discussed in earlier chapters on the development of drinking attitudes and behaviour and the context of family life and peer influence.

Fishbein and Ajzen's *theory of reasoned action* (Fishbein and Ajzen, 1975; Ajzen and Maddon, 1986) argues that people's behaviour can be accurately predicted by their stated intention to act in a certain way. Behavioural intentions are considered to be a product of an individual's beliefs, attitudes, evaluation of the consequences of a course of action, perceived social norms and perceived drinking skills. The influence of the drinking environment is assumed to be expressed through these variables. Applied to young people's drinking, this theory suggests that their actual drinking behaviour can be predicted by asking young people what they would do (including how much they would drink) in certain situations.

There is some empirical support for this model in relation to a variety of behaviours including smoking and drinking (Ajzen and Fishbein, 1980; Sutton, 1987). General objections to the model are that the causal relationship between attitudes, norms, self-efficacy and behaviour are rarely proved and that it excludes a persons experience, i.e. their current and past behaviour. In relation to young drinkers, MacAndrew and Edgerton (1970) pose a more fundamental objection – that it assumes that young people feel obliged to act in accordance with the beliefs and norms about drinking alcohol. From a cross-cultural perspective, they argue that the settings for drinking in Western cultures can be characterised as 'time out', or granting permission to ignore the normal social rules of behaviour. Thus they suggest that the model may not take into account the degree to which young people, when drinking outside of the home environment, feel free to behave in ways which are inconsistent with their attitudes, beliefs and norms. MacAndrew and Edgerton's argument is also supported by the analysis by Traeen and Kvalem (1996) of the function of alcohol in young people's sexual behaviour (see 'Alcohol and sexual risk-taking' in Chapter 6).

In acknowledging this cross-cultural perspective, some social researchers argue that *social and environmental influences* may be important in explaining young people's drinking behaviour. Supporters of this perspective do not suggest that such influences account for all variations in young people's drinking behaviour, but argue that the context and settings in which young people drink alcohol and the physical and social environment in which young people live have a greater significance than is acknowledged within the models described above. A growing body of evidence is accumulating to support this view. For example, a longitudinal study of influences on the drinking of 15-year-old New Zealanders found that situational characteristics, such as drinking location, who was present and time of day, explained a large amount of the variation in the amount of alcohol consumed (Connolly *et al.*, 1992).

An observational study of 16- to 20-year-olds in the Netherlands found that the drinking situation is a particularly important influence on young men's drinking (Van de Goor, Knibbe and Drop, 1990). This study found that young men tended to drink faster when music was played more loudly and when they were part of an all-male group. In contrast only the group influenced young women's drinking rates. Young women drank faster when drinks were bought in 'rounds' and when there was more movement in and out of the drinking group. A follow-up study (Knibbe, Oostveen and Van de Goor, 1991) set out to test whether the amount young people drank in public places, for example bars and discos, was due to reasoned behaviour or related to the situation. They found that for young men, the drinking situation contributed more to variations in consumption than their alcohol-specific beliefs, norms and self-efficacy. Frequency of visiting pubs, clubs, etc. was the most important factor for young men, with group pressure to drink and size of the drinking group also being important. For young women, perceptions that they could control their consumption when they were in different moods (i.e. when they felt tense, angry, cheerful and so on) and social norms were the factors most strongly correlated with consumption levels. This study also found that young people's perceived skills in being able to control their drinking in different drinking situations (such as when expected to buy a round, when offered a drink) contributed little to actually controlling consumption, when group pressure was experienced! An Australian study of occasions when young people consciously plan to binge drink also found that their perceived skills in handling drinking situations bore little relationship to their actual drinking behaviour (Gillespie *et al.*, 1991).

Despite the fact that most of young people's drinking (and that of adults) takes place during their leisure time, relatively little research has been done on unpicking the relationships between drinking and leisure. Kunz's review (1997) of the (mainly North American) literature found that most studies focused on special populations, for example college athletes, limiting their generalisability. Drinking patterns were crudely measured in leisure surveys, while leisure questions in alcohol surveys were equally unsophisticated, as found in Hendry and colleagues' work on young people's leisure and lifestyles in the UK (Hendry *et al.*,1993). To inform health promotion interventions, it would seem important to understand more about the leisure contexts that support both safe and risky drinking behaviour among young people.

These findings have important implications for alcohol education and point to the need for similar studies, to examine the influence of context and settings on the drinking behaviour of young people in Britain. British studies rarely make these variables the central focus of interest but some do make tantalising references to context or setting almost as an afterthought to the main report. For example, Shepherd, and Brinkley's study (1996) of young males injured in urban city centre violence found that all injuries took place within one postal code area and at least 85% of assaults took place in a bar or shortly after leaving one. The authors tentatively suggest that the settings for drinking might be appropriate targets for health promotion interventions. If social settings *do* have the degree of influence on young people's drinking behaviour that is suggested, then, as Knibbe, Oostveen and Van de Goor (1991) point out, educational interventions which are mainly aimed at changing individual attitudes and norms are not likely to achieve a relevant change in consumption levels. Interventions which seek to develop individual self-efficacy, in teaching skills to deal with different situations might help but these results suggest that effective interventions will also need to directly target and change the settings and environments where young people drink.

INTERPRETATIONS DERIVED FROM QUALITATIVE AND ETHNOGRAPHIC STUDIES

The theories described in 'Analytical studies' and 'Theories derived from analytical studies' above are largely derived from research within a scientific-positivist paradigm. Researchers working within an interpretivist philosophy consider young people's drinking to be socially and culturally defined rather than an objective fact. The purpose of research is seen as exploring how young people understand and make sense of their social world and the place and meaning of alcohol within it. Relatively few studies of this type have been conducted in Britain: a recent international collection of ethnographic studies on gender, drink and drugs included only one British study and this did not focus on young people (McDonald, 1994).

The few qualitative and ethnographic studies that are available lend further support to the view that the *social contexts* for young people's drinking are an important key to understanding alcohol's place and meaning. However, as work within an interpretivist framework acknowledges that young people's social worlds are diverse and local, care must be taken in extrapolating conclusions from these studies to young people in general. The recent UK studies available to date are by no means comprehensive. The young people studied include: convicted young offenders (Parker, 1996); young teenage street drinkers from relatively poor backgrounds in the North West (Brain and Parker, 1997); young pub drinkers in Newcastle city centre (Gofton, 1990) and Tameside (Tierney, Cohen and Bates, 1991); 15-year-olds living on the East Coast of Scotland (Pavis, Cunningham-Burley and Amos, 1997) and Hebridean youth culture (Dean, 1990). A focus group study conducted in 13 English towns, involving young people aged 13–20 (Mathrani, 1998) is also relevant, although the respondents in this study were recruited from a diverse range of social worlds. Some interpretations of young people's drinking can also be drawn from qualitative studies of other aspects of young people's health behaviour, such as Backett and Davison's work (1992) on the meaning of health and illness in different cultural settings, Hirst's study (1994) of young people's sexual risk-taking and Hirst and McCamley-Finney's study (1994) of young people's illicit drug use in Sheffield.

Some key themes emerge from these studies, many of which complement and reinforce understandings derived from descriptive surveys and analytical studies:

1. The functional nature of drinking

Young people drink because it meets their needs (or they perceive it to do so). Social interaction and peer approval are group processes that young people facilitate by drinking. Alcohol is also consciously used to alter mood.

2. The importance of the buzz

Young people consciously drink to get drunk.

3. The importance of the drinking group, settings and local networks

The group(s) in which young people drink and the settings for drinking are important mediators of drinking behaviour and its outcomes. The dynamic interaction between the individual and the group are gender, age and culture specific. Young people behave in different ways when drinking, according to the drinking environment (Van de Goor, Knibbe and Drop, 1990; Connolly *et al.*, 1992; Burns, 1980; Fox, 1997; Mathrani, 1998).

4. Drinking as hedonism

Pleasure seeking, having a good time, are features of young people's use of alcohol.

5. Drinking as time out

Some researchers suggest that for young people, unsupervised leisure time spent drinking alcohol is 'time out' from the social norms and expectations that would normally regulate their social behaviour. When intoxicated, young people expect to behave in ways that would not be acceptable if they were sober (Traeen and Kvalem, 1996; MacAndrew and Edgerton, 1970).

6. Drinking as consumerism

Young people, including younger teenagers, purchase and evaluate alcohol using the same sort of criteria as they would apply to any other consumer goods: flavour, value for money in achieving a buzz, selection of drinks and drinking styles which fit the image, style and fashion of youth culture (Gofton, 1990; Coffield and Gofton, 1994; Brain and Parker, 1997)

7. Drinking as part of leisure

Drinking alcohol is an integral part of young people's (and adults') leisure activities. Brain and Parker (1997) observe that young people in the 1990s purchase and consume leisure rather than create it for themselves. There are abundant leisure choices to be purchased, including fast food, cinemas, go-karting, amusement parks and thrill rides. Intoxicating substances (illegal drugs and alcohol) are purchased and consumed within this framework.

8. Drinking combined with illicit drug use

One of the biggest current changes to youth culture is the increasing normalisation of illicit drug use. Alcohol is evaluated and used within an ever-expanding repertoire of mind-altering substances (Parker and Measham, 1994; Hirst and McCamley-Finney, 1994).

9. Boundaries

In addition to group norms and dynamics, the amount of parental control, unsupervised time, spending power, school, tertiary education, sports, hobbies and employment, all regulate young people's use of alcohol. Young people whose lives have fewer boundaries will consequently have fewer boundaries to their drinking. For example, studies in the North west of England (Brain and Parker, 1997) and in Germany (Alheit, 1994) have found that young people who are unemployed or excluded from school have been observed to use alcohol to fill time and add structure and meaning to their day.

Conclusions

This review has summarised the descriptive studies on young people and alcohol. It has shown how young people acquire adult drinking habits as part of normal socialisation and has emphasised that youthful drinking is not deviant behaviour. It has also discussed the risks associated with young people's use of alcohol and noted that drinking patterns are changing among young people. Young people from the age of 11 up to young adults are drinking more alcohol, more frequently. Beverage choices have diversified in parallel with diversification of the drinks market. The gap between male and female drinking patterns is less among young people than in other age groups.

In England, public education about alcohol has until recently largely been aimed at adults. The HEA's Drinkwise campaign, 1989–94, promoted sensible drinking in the general adult population and achieved impressive improvements in public awareness and knowledge about units, measures and sensible drinking levels (Wright, 1995). Since 1997, the HEA has targeted young adults and an earlier version of this review has been used to inform this work. Within health services, until 1998, health promotion efforts at both national and local level have been directed at achievement of the targets for the Health of the Nation strategy. In the key area of coronary heart disease and stroke, the alcohol target was:

> 'To reduce the proportion of men drinking more than 21 units of
> alcohol per week from 28% in 1990 to 18% by 2005, and the
> proportion of women drinking more than 14 units of alcohol per week
> from 11% in 1990 to 7% by 2005.'
>
> (Department of Health, 1992)

Eighteen- to twenty-four-year-olds are the age group most likely to exceed these sensible drinking levels. The spotlight therefore fell on young people as a target group. In 1998, the Green Paper *Our Healthier Nation* continues the focus on young people, in setting out the Government's proposals for improving health and addressing health inequalities (Department of Health, 1998). There is less emphasis on target setting in the new strategy (there is no specific alcohol target) and greater acknowledgement of the social, economic and environmental determinants of ill health. Alcohol is specifically mentioned as an example of a lifestyle factor and within two of the four priority areas – accidents and mental health. The proposed target for accidents is to reduce the rate of accidents by at least a fifth by 2010 from a 1996 baseline. Alcohol is only mentioned in terms of drink driving, although its importance as a contributory factor in many other types of accident (see 'Accidents and injury' in Chapter 6) provides ample justification for prevention of alcohol misuse. This is particularly relevant to the health needs of children and young people, for whom accidents are the greatest single threat to life. Within the priority area of mental health, the proposed target is to reduce the death rate from suicide by at least a sixth by 2010 from a 1996 baseline. Given alcohol's association with depression and suicide in young people (see 'Alcohol and young people's mental health' in Chapter 6), a focus on preventing alcohol misuse by young people will continue to be an important element in national, regional and local health strategy.

This review raises a number of important issues for alcohol education with young people and prevention of alcohol misuse. Its findings and these conclusions should be considered in the light of the conclusions reached by the parallel review of effectiveness studies undertaken by Foxcroft, Lister-Sharp and Lowe (1997). Taken together the two reviews provide a picture of our current understanding of young people's drinking behaviour and of the effectiveness of alcohol education.

THE LIMITATIONS OF DESCRIPTIVE STUDIES

Since 1970, research on young people and alcohol has mainly employed quantitative, epidemiological and survey methods to accumulate a considerable body of information on alcohol-related problems and the distribution of alcohol consumption among British adolescents (May, 1992; Sharp and Lowe, 1989). This information has obvious value to those involved in health promotion and the prevention and treatment of alcohol misuse. However, it is insufficient to inform detailed interventions relevant to the needs of this particular target group. As May points out, 'the distribution of the behaviour is in no doubt, but explaining *why* it plays such an obviously central role in young people's lives may be of great value in explaining drinking behaviours in later life, as well as understanding problematic behaviour among the young' (p. 112).

YOUNG PEOPLE'S INTERPRETATION OF ALCOHOL EDUCATION

Much alcohol education uses language, methods and messages that are framed by adults, for adults. One notable exception to this is the HEA's *'Too much drink? THINK'* 1998 campaign materials which, while written by adults, are aimed at 13- to 17-year-olds and young adults, and have at least been piloted with the target groups. A series of postcards for 13- to 17-year-olds featuring four undesirable drinking situations uses young people's language – 'snog', 'prat', 'puke' and 'scrap'. The harm-reduction approach used with adult target groups is transferable to young people. Given the normality of drinking in Britain, young people will have little interest in abstinence. 'Sensible drinking' and 'moderation' messages hold little appeal to young people and may not be interpreted in the way adults intend, as suggested by Hanmer-Lloyd's research (1989) and the HEA's (1994) study of sensible drinking messages in black and minority ethnic groups.

How young people perceive, interpret, structure and act on alcohol education messages has to date mainly been explored in terms of their general knowledge and attitudes. For example, it would be useful to know how young people interpret the term 'moderation' and whether white young people share the view held by young people from minority ethnic groups (HEA, 1994), that moderation means not showing drunken behaviour. The interpretations of 'safe places to drink alcohol' made by young people who were members of the Portman Group's panel meetings (Fox, 1997) suggest that we need to acknowledge that young people see drinking in their social worlds in different ways to adults. Research to explore young people's interpretations of key alcohol education messages would seem to be an important prerequisite for planning appropriate interventions.

DRINKING PATTERNS

The review has identified heavy drinking sessions or 'binge drinking' as particularly prevalent in young people. They are also more tolerant of drunkenness. Deliberately seeking intoxication is the norm within some groups of young people (Gofton, 1990), and in certain social settings and occasions (Gillespie *et al.*, 1991; Knibbe, Oostveen and Van de Goor, 1991). Pre-1995 advice on weekly sensible drinking levels did not address the risks of binge drinking and targeting only heavier drinkers will not include all young people who binge drink. It can be argued that a single binge drinking session will place those young people involved at increased risk of certain types of alcohol-related harm (for example impaired decision-making, accidents, injury, unconsciousness or death), *particularly* if they are novice drinkers or normally drink small amounts, infrequently.

Alcohol education clearly needs to address these drinking patterns because of the risks attached to them. To appeal to young people, strategies must acknowledge *why* young people get drunk and the part drinking and getting drunk plays in their social worlds. In North America, there is a growing body of data on drinking norms among young people (Greenfield and Room, 1997). With the exception of the HEA's focus group study (Mathrani, 1998) we have little information about social norms for drunken behaviour among different ages and cultural groups of young people in Britain, for example what kinds of drunken behaviour, and levels of intoxication are expected, tolerated or meet with disapproval.

We also have little information about the self-control strategies that young people normally adopt to limit their drinking, apart from knowing that only a small minority of young people (and adults) monitor their weekly alcohol consumption (BMRB, 1994), and that driving is an acceptable excuse for not drinking (Mathrani, 1998). Such information has proved useful in informing interventions with problem drinkers (for example Yates, 1994) and could be useful in developing primary prevention strategies which take young people's current experience as their starting point. McMurran and Whitman (1990) identified three major groups of self-control strategies which young offenders had successfully used to control their drinking, unaided by any formal help. These were social change (for example avoiding heavy drinking friends), setting limits (for example limiting expenditure on drink) and rate control (for example eating before drinking). Further research could usefully identify the self-control strategies used by young people in general and at different ages and stages in their drinking careers.

THE PLACE AND MEANING OF DRINKING IN YOUNG PEOPLE'S LIVES

The studies reported here indicate that young people's drinking behaviour and its consequences are a complex interplay of individual, interpersonal and environmental factors, which are culturally specific. This complexity is acknowledged in the government's draft health strategy *Our Healthier Nation*. Despite the abundance of descriptive information on young people's drinking, we still know relatively little about how drinking practices fit into adolescent social worlds, the meaning of drinking to different groups of young people of various ages and cultural backgrounds, the norms and rules that govern their drinking behaviour and how young people's norms and rules compare with those of adults. Do young people drink like adults or do adults drink like young people?

The need to explore the place and meaning of drinking in young women's lives is a particular priority because it appears that gender differences in frequency and consumption may be diminishing. It would therefore seem important to understand a great deal more about *why* young women's drinking is converging with that of young men. We know little of the meanings attached to alcohol use and the value placed on this activity by young women in Britain. For example, a recent collection of anthropological studies on gender, alcohol and drugs (McDonald, 1994) provides more information about young women's drinking in Japan, Fiji and Southern Sudan than it does about young women in Britain.

Another priority for research is to extend the HEA's small-scale work on sensible drinking messages in a multi-cultural society (HEA, 1994) and its surveys of the health of schoolchildren (Turtle, Jones and Hickman, 1997) to address more fully the needs of young people from different ethnic groups. We know very little about their experience of growing up in a youth culture where drinking is the norm, nor of the religious, cultural and family conflicts they may experience.

TARGET GROUPS

To achieve the *Our Healthier Nation* targets, one strategy would be to target specifically young people who are heavy drinkers. This strategy is supported by the alcohol industry and by some researchers (for example Plant, Bagnall and Foster, 1990). However, Edwards *et al.* (1994) have produced substantial international evidence that, to reduce the overall burden of alcohol problems in England, a general population approach is required to reduce overall consumption levels. The fact that risky drinking among young people is not confined to those who exceed adult sensible drinking levels, supports the argument for alcohol education aimed at all young people and not just the heavy drinkers. Moreover, preventive measures that influence all young people will also have an impact on those who are heavy or problem drinkers (Edwards *et al.*, 1994).

Alcohol education targeting young people will need to take account of the fact that they are not a homogeneous group. This review has summarised the development of young people's drinking through three age groups: the under-16s, 16–17s and 18–24s. There are major differences in drinking knowledge, attitudes and behaviour between the three age groups, particularly between younger adolescents and the over-16s and between pre-pub drinking and drinking in licensed premises. A spiral curriculum for alcohol education, in either formal or informal settings, should show depth and progression appropriate to the age, stage and drinking experience of the young people involved. In terms of alcohol education materials, some resources have been developed which achieve this (for example 'Six pack' for youth work (Wright, 1995), *Alcohol Education Syllabus* for secondary schools (TACADE, 1987, now out of print), but the same principle also applies to mass media campaigns aimed at young people. The socio-demograpic, geographic, religious and cultural variations in young people's drinking described in this review also need to be acknowledged. This implies appropriate baseline research with identified populations of young people before interventions are implemented.

Parents are an important target group. Lowe, Foxcroft and Sibley (1993) have demonstrated that family life continues to have a strong influence on young people's drinking behaviour during adolescence and young adulthood. Balding's comment (1989) 'we teach them how to drink' would seem to be an appropriate message for parents, particularly to those parents who are unaware of the importance of family influence.

Peer group cultures are also important targets for alcohol education, particularly in challenging norms which support the risky drinking of group members, such as approval of drinking to get very drunk, or group endorsement of violent or antisocial behaviour when intoxicated.

Targeting young people who have a high disposable *income* would seem to be appropriate because of the association of income with consumption levels. Consequently the *workplace* will be an appropriate setting for alcohol education aimed at young people. While *tax increases* would certainly not be popular with young people, it can be predicted that increasing the price of alcohol is likely to have its greatest impact on the consumption levels of those young people who have the least money to spend, for example the unemployed and those in full-time education.

MESSAGES

To address risky drinking behaviour, it is not what young people know about alcohol, but what they do with that knowledge that is important. Health educators might usefully consider not only what young people need to know, but also why they need to know it. In seeking to reduce or minimise experience of alcohol-related harm and risk-taking by young people, it will be necessary not only to provide information but also to develop the cognitive skills that enable young people to use alcohol information.

Coffield and Gofton (1994) argue that when drinking, young people construct a mental 'balance sheet' of the costs and benefits of drinking which will include what they know about alcohol. This is the foundation of motivational theory and motivational interviewing techniques (Miller and Rollnick, 1991) which are used in preparing people to change addictive behaviours. The balance sheet approach could also be used in primary prevention among young people, so that they perceive less benefit in risky drinking and higher costs. This strategy would require clarity in identifying what young people at different ages and stages define as risky drinking.

'Costs' that might be emphasised could include the immediate negative consequences of intoxication and the potential impact of impaired decision-making and social skills on young people's social relationships. The negative image of the heavy drinker might be highlighted, as might the impact of heavy drinking on physical fitness and appearance. Financial costs will also be important to young people.

'Benefits' of low-risk drinking which might be promoted could include emphasising the converse of the consequences described under 'costs', the ability to achieve social and personal goals, enhanced personal style and image, and taking individual responsibility for behaviour.

Given that young people's drinking is so closely associated with friendship, social and sexual relationships, it would seem important to acknowledge this in alcohol education messages and strategies. For example one strategy favoured by young drug users who participated in a peer led project to make animated cartoons (TACADE, 1994) was 'looking after your mates'. Alcohol education should emphasis what young people value in their social relationships.

Alcohol education messages need to challenge young people's attitudes, expectations and perceptions of social norms that support risky drinking. One of the most important is young people's greater acceptance of drunkenness. Most of the common expectancies associated with drinking could also be challenged: appearing adult, enhancing sexuality and social interaction, increased assertiveness and aggression. Perceived risks might also be addressed, because young people do not consider the more serious consequences of binge drinking to be very likely (Gillespie *et al.*, 1991). It may be possible to promote behaviour change by emphasising the inconsistencies *within* young people's alcohol-related attitudes and behaviour and *between* these and other attitudes and values. For example most young people hold strong negative attitudes to drinking and driving, yet they may ride in a vehicle with an intoxicated driver, particularly if their own judgement is impaired by alcohol (Mayberry and Clark, 1991). Similarly, desire to appear adult, fashionable or 'cool' may not be consistent with the indignity of being sick, soiled clothing, falling over or becoming unconscious as a consequence of drinking.

While a harm reduction approach is likely to be most acceptable to young people, it will also be important to give clear guidance about circumstances in which *no* alcohol should be drunk. The image of the non-drinker continues to be negative in the eyes of young people, except when driving. Health education messages could seek to increase the social acceptability of non-drinking by young people. This has already been exploited successfully in relation to drink-driving campaigns and could be extended to other common activities in young people's lives, for example when playing computer games, revising for examinations, doing sports, operating machinery. Such initiatives might elicit the support of the non-alcoholic drinks industry. More participative research like that of McLaughlin (1989) and Mathrani (1998) is required, to identify the occasions and social situations when non-drinking is considered the most acceptable by young people of different backgrounds and ages.

SITUATIONAL AND ENVIRONMENTAL APPROACHES

The research on social context suggests that interventions that aim to modify the drinking environment might have considerable potential for influencing both consumption levels and the outcomes of drinking among young people. The study by Knibbe, Oostveen and Van de Goor (1991) suggests that this approach may be more effective in reducing consumption than interventions aimed at individual young people. The HEA directly targeted the drinking environment as part of its Drinkwise campaign and has experience of the problems and pitfalls of this type of intervention. Local alcohol educators who participated in Drinkwise clearly found this approach difficult to implement (Wright, 1995) and as yet there are few evaluations of situational approaches (but see Tierney, Cohen and Bates, 1991). Jeffs and Saunders' account (1983) of the positive impact of increased police enforcement of the licensing laws on the levels of alcohol-related crime and disorder in an English seaside town demonstrates the potential of this approach. Another more recent initiative is the move to persuade licensees to serve alcohol in unbreakable glasses in order to reduce 'glassing' injuries. Use of closed circuit television in town centres has been an effective deterrent to violence on the streets.

The realities of young people's lives, with all their variables, have not been used to inform health education initiatives (Smith and Harding, 1989; Hirst, 1994). Most alcohol education is planned, delivered and evaluated by adult professionals, based on their notions of young people's realities. Young people's drinking behaviours are presented as a set of worrying statistics, viewed in isolation from the rest of their lives. This review has identified a need for research, which locates these statistics of alcohol-related harm within the broader needs, experiences, cultures and values of young people. It suggests ways in which alcohol education might be more closely based on young people's leisure and lifestyles and highlights the importance of addressing the drinking environment as well as targeting young people themselves.

References

Aas, H. and Pedersen, W. (1993). Stages in adolescents' drug use – a longitudinal study. *Nordisk Alkohtidsskrift* **10**(3): 145–54.

Aggleton, P. (1996). *Health Promotion and Young People*. London: Health Education Authority.

Ahmed, N. (1988). Uncovering a hidden problem. *Alcohol Concern* **4** (1): 8–9.

Aitken, P. P. (1978). *Ten to Fourteen Year Olds and Alcohol*. Edinburgh: HMSO.

Ajzen, I. and Fishbein, M. (1980). *Understanding Attitudes and Predicting Social Behaviour*. New York: Prentice Hall.

Ajzen, I. and Maddon, J. T. (1986). Prediction of goal directed behaviour: attitudes, intentions and perceived behavioural control. *Journal of Experimental Social Research*. **22**: 453–74.

Alcohol Concern (1991). *Alcohol Can Damage Your Health*. London: Alcohol Concern.

Alcohol Concern (1994). *Alcohol and Accidents. Factsheet*. London: Alcohol Concern.

Alcohol (1996a). *Pop Fiction? The truth about Alcopops*. London: Alcohol Concern.

Alcohol Concern (1996b). *Alcohol and Crime: Information Pack*. London: Alcohol Concern.

Alcohol Concern (1997a). Submission to the Acheson Inquiry on Health Inequalities. Unpublished Paper.

Alcohol Concern (1997b). *Measures for Measures: A Framework for Alcohol Policy*. London: Alcohol Concern.

Alcohol Concern (1997c). *Factsheet No. 9. Drinking and Driving*. London: Alcohol Concern.

Alheit, P. (1994). *Taking the Knocks*. London: Cassell.

Anderson, P. (1984). Alcohol consumption of undergraduates at Oxford University. Alcohol and Alcoholism **19**: 77–84

Anderson, P., Cremona, A., Paton, A., Turner, C. and Wallace, P. (1993). The risk of alcohol. *Addiction*. **88**: 1493–1508.

Andreasson, S., Allebeck, P. and Romelsjö, A. (1990). Hospital admissions for somatic care among young men: the role of alcohol. *British Journal of Addiction* **85**: 935–41.

Asad, A. (1994). *A Report on the Patterns of Drinking and Associated Problems within the Bangladeshi Community in Tower Hamlets*. London: Inform-Al/Bangladeshi Alcohol Services Development Project.

Backett, K. and Davison, C. (1992). Rational or reasonable? Perceptions of health at different stages of life. *Health Education Journal* **51** (2): 55–9.

Bagnall, G. (1991). *Educating Young Drinkers*. London: Routledge.

Balding, J. (1989). *We Teach Them How to Drink!* Exeter: Schools Health Education Unit, University of Exeter.

Balding, J. (1996). *Very Young People in 1993–5*. Exeter: Schools Health Education Unit, University of Exeter.

Balding, J. (1994). *Young People in 1993*. Exeter: Schools Health Education Unit, University of Exeter.

Balding, J. (1995). *Young People in 1994*. Exeter: Schools Health Education Unit, University of Exeter.

Balding, J. (1997). *Young People in 1996*. Exeter: Schools Health Education Unit, University of Exeter.

Balding J., Regis, D., Wise, A., Bish, D and Muirden, J. (1997). *Young People and Alcohol: its use and abuse*. Exeter: Schools Health Education Unit, University of Exeter.

Balding, J. and Shelley, C. (1993). *Very Young People in 1992*. Exeter: Schools Health Education Unit, University of Exeter.

Baldwin, S. (ed.) (1990). *Alcohol Education and Offenders*. London: Batsford.

Bandura, A. (1977). *Social Learning Theory*. Englewood Cliffs, New York: Prentice Hall.

Bean, P., Wilkinson, C. K., Whynes, D. K. and Giggs, J. A. (1988). Knowledge of drugs and consumption of alcohol among Nottingham 15 year olds. *Health Education Journal* 47 (2/3): 79–82.

Beattie, J. O., Hull, D., Cockburn, F. (1986). Children intoxicated by alcohol in Nottingham and Glasgow. *British Medical Journal* 292: 519–21.

Bennet, P., Smith, C. and Nugent, Z. (1989). *Drinking Patterns and Knowledge of Alcohol in Wales*, 1989. Cardiff: Health Promotion Authority for Wales.

Bennett, N., Jarvis, L., Rowlands, O., Singleton, N. and Haselden, L. (1996). *Living in Britain: Results from the 1994 General Household Survey*. OPCS. London: HMSO.

Black, D. and Weare, K. (1989). Knowledge and attitudes about alcohol in 17 and 18 year olds. *Health Education Journal* 48 (2): 69–74.

B M R B (1991). *Report of a Telephone Omnibus Survey: Pub of the Future*. Report to HEA. Unpublished.

B M R B (1994). *Communications Monitor, Drinkwise 1994*. (Post) Report to HEA. Unpublished.

161

Boyns, M. (1993). *What Do They Know about Alcohol? Summary Report of the Main Findings of the 1993 Survey of Pembrokeshire 12–13 year olds' Drinking Knowledge, Behaviour and Beliefs.* Camarthen, Dyfed: Alcohol Advisory Service.

Brain, K. and Parker, H. (1997). *Drinking with Design: Alcopops, Designer Drinks and Youth Culture.* London: The Portman Group.

Brisby, T., Baker, S. and Hedderwick, T. (1997) *Under the Influence: Coping with Parents who Drink Too Much.* A report on the needs of children of problem drinking parents. London: Alcohol Concern.

Brown, S. A., Goldman, M. S., Inn, A. and Anderson, L. R. (1980). Expectancies of reinforcement from alcohol: their domain and relation to drinking patterns. *Journal of Consulting and Clinical Psychology* **48**: 419–26.

Burns, T. F. (1980). Getting rowdy with the boys. *Journal of Drug Issues* **10**: 273–86.

Cochrane, R. (1989). *Drinking Problems in Minority Ethnic Groups.* Birmingham: University of Birmingham School of Psychology.

Coffield, F. J. and Gofton, L. (1994). *Drugs and Young People.* London: Institute for Public Policy Research.

Coggans, N. and McKellar, S. (1994). Drug use amongst peers: peer pressure or peer preference. *Drugs: Education, Prevention and Policy* **1**(1): 15–25.

Coggans, N. and McKellar, S. (1995). *The Facts about Alcohol, Aggression and Adolescence.* London: Cassell.

Coggans, N., Shewan, D., Henderson, M. and Davies, J. B. (1991). The Impact of School-based drug education. *British Journal of Addiction* **86**: 1099–109.

Coleman, R. and Cassell, D. (1995). Parents who misuse drugs and alcohol. In Reder, P. and Lucey, C. (eds). *Assessment of Parenting: Psychiatric and Psychological Contributions.* London: Routledge.

Collier, D. J. and Beales, I. L. P. (1989). Drinking among medical students: a questionnaire survey. *British Medical Journal* **299**: 19–22.

Connolly, G. M., Casswell, S., Stewart, J. and Silva, P. (1992). Drinking context and other influences on the drinking of 15 year old New Zealanders. *British Journal of Addiction* **87**: 1029–36.

Connolly, G. M., Casswell, S., Zhang, J. F. and Silva, P. A. (1994). Alcohol in the mass media and drinking by adolescents: a longitudinal study. *Addiction* **89**: 1255–63.

Craig, J., Francis, D. and McWhirter, L. (1991). *Smoking and Drinking amongst 11–15 year-olds in Northern Ireland in 1990*. Belfast: HMSO.

Craig, T., Hodson, S., Richardson, S., and Woodward, S. (1996). *Off to a Bad Start, a Longitudinal Study of Homeless Young People in London*. London: Mental Health Foundation.

Crawford, A. and Allsop, D. T. (1996). *Young People and Alcohol in Scotland: a Survey of Brand Preferences of 15–17 year olds conducted in February 1996*. Glasgow: Scottish Council on Alcohol.

Cummins, L. H. (1961). Hypoglycaemia and convulsions in children following alcoholic ingestion. *Journal of Paediatrics* **58**: 23–6.

Davies, J. B. (1992). Peer group influence and youthful alcohol consumption: an opinion. In *Alcohol and Young People: Learning to Cope*. Proceedings of Addictions Forum, Alcohol Research Group Conference, October 1992. London: The Portman Group.

Davies, J. B. and Coggans, N. (1991). The Facts about Adolescent Drug Abuse. London: Cassell.

Davies, J. B. and Stacey, B. (1972). *Teenagers and Alcohol: a Developmental Study in Glasgow*. London: HMSO.

Dean, A. (1990). Culture and Community: drink and soft drugs in Hebridean Youth Culture. *Sociological Review* **38**: 517–63.

Denney, R. C. (1986) *Alcohol and Accidents* Wilmslow: Sigma Press.

Denney, R. C. (1997). *None for the Road*. Crayford, Kent: Shaw and Sons.

Denscombe, M. (1995). Ethnic group and alcohol consumption: the case of 15–16 year olds in Leicestershire. *Public Health* **109**: 133–42.

Department for Education (1995). *Science in the National Curriculum*. London: HMSO.

Department of Health (1992). *The Health of the Nation: a Strategy for Health in England*. London: HMSO.

Department of Health (1996). *Hospital Episode Statistics* 1994–5. London: HMSO.

Department of Health (1998). *Our Healthier Nation: a Contract for Health*. London: Stationery Office.

Department of Health (1995). *Sensible Drinking*. London: HMSO.

Department of Health and Social Services for Northern Ireland (1989). *Drinking among School Children in Northern Ireland*. Belfast: DHSS.

Deykin, D., Buka, S. and Zeena, T. (1992). Depressive illness among chemically dependent adolescents. *American Journal of Psychiatry* **149**: 1341–7.

Diamond, I. D., Pritchard, C., Choudry, N., Fielding, M., Cox, M. and Bushnell, D. (1988). The incidence of drug and solvent misuse among southern English normal comprehensive schoolchildren. *Public Health* **102**: 107–14.

Dight, S. (1976). *Scottish Drinking Habits*. London: HMSO.

Donovan, C. and McEwan, R. (1995). A review of the literature examining the relationship between alcohol use and HIV-related sexual risk taking in young people. *Addiction* **90**: 319–28.

Donovan, J. E. and Jessor, R. (1978). Adolescent problem drinking: psychosocial correlates in a national sample study. *Journal of Studies on Alcohol* **39**: 1506–24.

Dorn, N. (1983). *Alcohol, Youth and the State*. Oxford: Croom Helm.

Drinksense (1996). *Fenland Young People and their Alcohol Use*. Wisbech: Fenland Alcohol Service.

Edwards, G. *et al.* (1994). *Alcohol Policy and the Public Good*. Oxford: Oxford Medical.

Farrington, D. P. (1987). Epidemiology. In Tonny, M. and Morris, N. (eds) *Crime and Justice: an Annual Review of the Research, vol. 7.* Chicago: University of Chicago Press.

Fergusson, D. M., Lynskey, M. T. and Horwood, L. J. (1996). Alcohol misuse and juvenile offending in adolescence. *Addiction* **91**(4): 483–94.

Fishbein, M. and Ajzen, I. (1975). *Belief, Attitude, Intention and Behaviour: an Introduction to Theory and Research*. Reading, Mass.: Addison-Wesley.

Flanagan, J. (1997). *Survey of the Purchase and Use of alcohol by Young People in the Hambleton and Richmond Area*. Northallerton: North Yorkshire Health Promotion Service.

Flannigan, B., McLean, H. C. and Propp, V. (1990). Alcohol use: a situational influence on young women's pregnancy risk taking behaviours. *Adolescence* **25**: 205–15.

Forsyth, A. J. M., Barnard, M. and McKeganey, N. P. (1997). Alcopop supernova. Are alcoholic lemonades (alcopops) responsible for under-age drunkenness? *International Journal of Health Education* **35** (2): 1–6.

Fossey, E. (1992). The development of attitudes to alcohol in young children. In *Alcohol and Young People: Learning to Cope*. Proceedings of Addictions Forum, Alcohol Research Group Conference, October 1992. London: The Portman Group.

Fossey, E. (1994). *Growing up with Alcohol*. London: Routledge.

Fox, K. (1997). *Taskforce on Underage Alcohol Misuse: Report on the under-18 Panel Meetings*. London: The Portman Group.

Foxcroft, D., Lister-Sharp, D. and Lowe, G. (1997). Alcohol misuse prevention for young people: a systematic review reveals methodological concerns and lack of reliable evidence of effectiveness. *Addiction* **92**(5): 531–7.

Foxcroft, D. R. and Lowe, G. (1991). Adolescent drinking behaviour and family socialisation factors: a meta analysis. *Journal of Adolescence* **14**: 255–73.

Foxcroft, D. R. and Lowe, G. (1993). Self attributions for alcohol use on older teenagers. *Addiction Research* **1**: 1–9.

Foxcroft, D., Lowe, G. and Lister-Sharp, D. J. (1995). Teenage drinking: a four year comparative study. *Alcohol and Alcoholism* **30**(6): 713–19.

Foxcroft, D. R., Lowe, G. and May, C. (1994). Adolescent alcohol use and family influences: attributive statements by teenage drinkers. *Drugs: Education Prevention and Policy* **1** (1): 63–9.

Gagnon, J. H. and Simon, W. (1977). *Sexual Conduct: the Social Sources of Human Sexuality*. Hawthorne, New York: Aldine de Gruyter.

Gaines, L. S., Brook, P. H., Maisto, S., Dietrich, M. and Shagena, S. (1988). The development of children's knowledge of alcohol and the role of drinking. *Journal of Applied Developmental Psychology* **9**: 441–57.

Ghosh, S. K. (1984). Prevalence of drinking alcohol and alcohol dependence in the Asian population in the UK. In Krasner, S. J., Maddon, J. S. and Walker, R. J. (eds). *Alcohol related problems: Room for Manoeuvre*. Chichester: Wiley.

Gillespie, A., Davey, J., Sheenan, M. and Stedson, D. (1991). Thrills without spills: the educational implications of research into adolescent binge drinking for a school based intervention. *Drug Education Journal of Australia* **5**: 121–7.

Glassner, B. and Loughlin, J. (1987). *Drugs in Adolescent Worlds: Burnouts to Straights*. Basingstoke: Macmillan.

Goddard, E. (1991). *Drinking in England and Wales in the late 1980s*. London: HMSO.

Goddard, E. (1998). *Getting Drunk: Public Attitudes and Behaviour in England in 1997*. Report to the HEA. London: HEA. Unpublished.

Goddard, E. (1996). *Teenage Drinking in 1994*. London: HMSO.

Goddard, E. (1992). Young people's drinking. In *Alcohol and Young People: Learning to Cope*. Proceedings of Addictions Forum, Alcohol Research Group Conference, October 1992. London: The Portman Group.

Goddard, E. (1997a). *Young Teenagers and Alcohol in 1996, Volume 1: England*. Office for National Statistics. London: Stationery Office.

Goddard, E. (1977b). *Young Teenagers and Alcohol in 1996, Volume 2: Scotland*. Office for National Statistics. London: Stationery Office.

Gofton, L. (1990). On the town: drink and the new lawlessness. *Youth and Policy* **29**: 33–9.

Gold, R., Karmiloff-Smith, A. and Skinner, M. J. (1992). Situational factors and thought processes associated with unprotected intercourse in heterosexual students. *AIDS Care* **4**: 305–23.

Gold R., and Skinner, M. J. (1992). Situational factors and thought processes associated with unprotected intercourse in young gay men. *AIDS* **6** 1021–30.

Golub, A. and Johnson, B. D. (1994). The shifting importance of alcohol and marihuana as gateway substances among serious drug abusers. *Journal of Studies on Alcohol* **55**: 607–14.

Gordon, C., Carey, M. and Carey, K. (1997). Effects of a drinking event on behavioural skills and condom attitudes in men: implications for HIV risk from a controlled experiment. *Health Psychology* September **16**(5): 490–5.

Gould, P. (1997). Put up or shut up. *Drinks International*, February: 5.

Greenfield, T. K. and Room, R. (1997). Situational norms for drinking and drunkenness: trends in the United States adult population 1979–1990. *Addiction* **92**(1): 33–48.

Grube, J. W. and Wallack, L. (1994). The effects of television beer advertising on children. *American Journal of Public Health* **84**: 254–9.

Hanmer-Lloyd, S. (ed.) (1989). *Market Research and Alcohol Education*. Bristol: School of Advanced Urban Studies, University of Bristol.

Hansbro, J., Bridgwood, A., Morgan, A. and Hickman, A. (1997). *Health in England 1966: what people know, what people think, what people do*. London: HMSO.

Hansen, A. (1984). *The Portrayal of Alcohol and Drinking on Prime Time Television*. Leicester: Centre for Mass Communication Research.

Harford, T. C. and Grant, B. (1987). Psychosocial factors in adolescent drinking contexts. *Journal of Studies on Alcohol* **48**: 551–7.

Hastings, G. B., MacKintosh, A. M. and Aitken, P. P. (1992). Is alcohol advertising reaching the people it shouldn't reach? *Health Education Journal* **51**(1): 38–42.

Hawker, A. (1978). *Adolescents and Alcohol*. London: Edsall.

Hawton, K., Fagg, J., Platt, S. and Hawkins, M. (1993). Factors associated with suicide after parasuicide in young people. *British Medical Journal* **306**:1641–44.

Hayden, D. (1995). *Young people and alcohol related incidents*. Executive Summary Number 45 (4) London: Centre for Research on Drugs and Health Behaviour.

HEA (1990). *Alcohol Labelling Awareness Study*. Unpublished.

HEA (1994). *'Sensible Drinking': Messages in a Multicultural Society*. London: HEA.

HEA (1997). *Health update: Alcohol*. London: HEA.

HEA/MORI (1992a). *Today's Young Adults*. London: HEA.

HEA/MORI (1992b). *Tomorrow's Young Adults*. London: HEA.

HEA/RSGB (1991). *Omnibus Survey on Home Drinking*. Report to the HEA. Unpublished.

Hendry, L. B., Shucksmith, J., Love, J. G. and Glendinning, A. (1993). *Young People's Leisure and Lifestyles*. London: Routledge.

Hingson, R. and Howland, J. (1993). Alcohol and non-traffic unintended injuries. Addiction **88**: 877–83.

Hirst, J. (1994). Not in Front of the Grown Ups. Sheffield: Pavic Publications.

Hirst, J. and McCamley-Finney, A. (1994). *The Place and Meaning of Drugs in Young People's Lives*. Sheffield: Sheffield Hallam University.

Home Office (1996a). *Aspects of Crime: drunkenness, 1995*. London: Home Office.

Home Office (1996b) *Statistical Bulletin: The 1996 Crime Survey, England and Wales*. London: Home Office.

Home Office Standing Conference on Prevention (1987). Report of the Working Group on Young People and Alcohol. London: HMSO.

HPANI (1994). *Health Behaviour of Schoolchildren in Northern Ireland*. Belfast: Health Promotion Agency for Northern Ireland.

HPANI (1995) *Health Behaviour of Schoolchildren in Northern Ireland*: a Report of the 1994 Survey. Belfast: Health Promotion Agency for Northern Ireland.

Hughes, K., Mackintosh, A. M., Hastings, G., Wheeler, C., Watson, J. and Inglis, J. (1997). Young people, alcohol, and designer drinks: quantitative and qualitative study. *British Medical Journal* **314** (8 February): 414–18.

Hutchison, I. L., Magennis, P., Shepherd, J. P. and Brown, A. E. (1998). The BAOMS United Kingdom Survey of Facial Injuries, Part 1: Aetiology and the association with alcohol consumption. *British Journal of Oral and Maxillofacial Surgery* 36 (February): 4–14.

Ianotti, R. J. and Bush, P. J. (1992). Perceived use, actual friends' use of alcohol, cigarettes, marijuana and cocaine: which has the most influence? *Journal of Youth and Adolescence.* 21: 375–89.

Ianotti, R. J., Bush, P. J. and Weinfurt, K. P. (1996). Perception of friends' use of alcohol, cigarettes and marijuana among urban schoolchildren: a longitudinal analysis. *Addictive Behaviours* 21(5): 615–32.

ICAP (1997). The limits of binge drinking: ICAP Reports 2. *Alcohol Update* 32: 8–10. Glasgow: Scottish Council on Alcohol.

ISDD (1997). *Drug Misuse in Britain. 1996.* London: ISDD.

Jahoda, G. and Crammond, J. (1972). *Children and Alcohol: a Developmental Study in Glasgow.* London: HMSO.

Jeffs, B. W. and Saunders, W. M. (1983). Minimising alcohol-related offences by enforcement of the existing licensing legislation. *British Journal of Addiction* 78: 67–77.

Jessor, R., Chase, J. A. and Donovan, J. E. (1980). Psychosocial correlates of marijuana use and problem drinking: a national sample of adolescents. *American Journal of Public Health* 70: 604–13.

Jessor, R., Donovan, J. E. and Costa, F. M. (1991). *Beyond Adolescence.* Cambridge: Cambridge University Press.

Jessor, R. and Jessor, S. L. (1977). *Problem Behaviour and Psychosocial Development: a Longitudinal Study of Youth.* New York: Academic Press.

Kandel, D. B. (ed.) (1978). *Longitudinal Research on Drug Use.* New York: Halstead.

Karlsson, G. and Romelsjo, A. (1997). A longitudinal study of social, psychological and behavioural factors associated with drunken driving and public drunkenness. *Addiction* 92(4): 447–57.

Kemm, J. R. and Rowe, C. (1992). Do people understand 'units of alcohol'? *Health Education Journal* 51(2): 59–63.

Klein, H. and Pittman, J. (1993). The relationship between emotional state and alcohol consumption. *International Journal of the Addictions*. 28:47–61.

Knibbe, R. A., Oostveen, T. and Van de Goor, I. (1991). Young people's alcohol consumption in public places: reasoned behaviour or related to the situation? *British Journal of Addiction* 86: 1425–33.

Kohli, H. S. (1989). A comparison of smoking and drinking among Asian and white school children in Glasgow. *Public Health* 103: 433–9.

Kunz, J. L. (1997). Associating leisure with drinking: current research and future directness. *Drug and Alcohol Review* 16(1): 69–76.

Lader, D. and Matheson, J. (1991). *Smoking among Secondary School Children in 1990*. London: HMSO.

Lamninpaa, A., Vilska, J., Korri, U. M. and Riihimaki, V. (1993). Alcohol intoxication in hospitalised young teenagers. *Acta Paediatrica Scandinavica* 82: 773–8.

Lavik, N., Clausen, S. and Pedersen, W. (1991). Eating behaviour, drug use, psychopathology and parental bonding in adolescents in Norway. *Acta Psychiatrica Scandinavica* 84: 387–90.

Laybourn, A., Brown, J. and Hill, M. (1996). *Hurting on the Inside: Children's Experiences of Parental Alcohol Misuse*. Aldershot: Avebury.

Leigh, B. C. (1990a). The relationship of sex-related alcohol expectancies to alcohol consumption and sexual behaviour. *British Journal of Addiction* 85: 919–28.

Leigh, B. C. (1990b). The relationship of substance use during sex to high-risk sexual behaviour. *The Journal of Sex Research* **27**: 199–213.

Lewthwaite, P. (1990) *Young People's Health Choices Project.* Durham: Durham Health Authority.

Lister-Sharp, D. (1994). Underage drinking in the United Kingdom since 1970: public policy, the law and adolescent drinking behaviour. *Alcohol and Alcoholism* **29**(5): 555–63.

Lord President's Report (1991). *The Lord President's Report on Action against Alcohol Misuse.* London: HMSO.

Loretto, W. A. (1994). Youthful drinking in Northern Ireland and Scotland: preliminary results from a comparative study. *Drugs: education, prevention and policy* **1**(2): 143–52.

Lowe, G., Foxcroft, D. R. and Sibley, D. (1993). *Adolescent Drinking and Family Life.* Reading: Harwood Academic.

MacAndrew, C. and Edgerton, R. B. (1970). *Drunken Comportment: A Social Explanation.* London: Nelson.

McCall, M. (1997). The effects of physical attractiveness on gaining access to alcohol: when social policy meets social decision making. *Addiction* **92**(5): 597–600.

McDonald, M. (ed.) (1994). *Gender, Drink and Drugs.* Oxford: Berg.

McElduff, P. and Dobson, A. J. (1997). How much alcohol and how often? *British Medical Journal* **314** (19 April): 1159–64.

McEwan, R., McCallum, T., Bhopal, R. and Madhok, R. (1991). Sex and the risk of HIV infection: the role of alcohol. *British Journal of Addiction* **87**: 577–84.

McGuffin, S. (1979). Drinking patterns of young people in Northern Ireland. *Ulster Medical Journal* **48**(2): 26–30.

McKechnie, R., Cameron, D., Cameron, I. and Drewery, J. (1977). Teenage drinking in South West Scotland. *British Journal of Addiction* **72**: 287–95.

McKeganey, N. Forsyth, A., Barnard, M. and Hay, G. (1996). Designer drinks. *British Medical Journal* **313** (17 April): 401.

McLaughlin, D. (1989). Young people and an alcohol free way of life. *Health Education Journal* **48**(3): 134–6.

McMahon, J., Jones, B. T. and O'Donnell, P. (1994). Comparing positive and negative alcohol expectancies in male and female social drinkers. *Addiction Research* **1**: 349–65.

McMurran, M. (1992). Young offenders and alcohol: What do we know and what do we do about it? Paper presented at TACADE Conference, Young Offenders and Alcohol: Strategies and Services, Coventry, September 1992.

McMurran, M. and Hollin, C. (1993). *Young Offenders and Alcohol Related Crime*. Chichester: Wiley.

McMurran, M. and Whitman, J. (1990). Strategies of self control in male young offenders who have reduced their alcohol consumption without formal intervention. *Journal of Adolescence* **13**: 115–28.

McNeill, A., Harris, S., Kelly, M., Raw, M. and Kelly, G. (in preparation). *A survey of young people and new alcoholic drinks*.

Makela, P., Valkonen, T. and Martelin, T. (1997). Contribution of deaths related to alcohol use to socioeconomic variation in mortality: register based follow up study. *British Medical Journal* **315** (26 July): 211–6.

Maloff, D., Becker, H. S., Fonaroff, A. and Rodin, J. (1979). Informal social controls and their influences on substance misuse. *Journal of Drug Issues* **9**: 161–84.

Marlatt, G. A. and Rohsenau, D. J. (1980). Cognitive processes in alcohol use: expectancy and the balanced placebo design. In Mello, N. K., (ed.) *Advances in Substance Abuse.* Stamford, Conn.: JAI Press, pp.159–99.

Marsh, A., Dobbs, J. and White, A. (1986). *Adolescent Drinking.* London: HMSO.

Marsh, P. and Fox Kibby, K. (1992). *Drinking and Public Disorder.* Oxford: MCM Research.

Mathrani, S. (1998). *Young Drinkers: a Qualitative Study.* Report to the HEA, based on research by Research Works Ltd. London: HEA.

May, C. (1992). A burning issue? Adolescent alcohol use in Britain 1970–1991. *Alcohol and Alcoholism* 50: 195–9.

May, C. (1993). Resistance to peer pressure: an inadequate basis for alcohol education. *Health Education Research* 8(2): 159–65.

Mayberry, D. and Clarke, V. (1991). Why do passengers ride with intoxicated drivers? *Drug Education Journal of Australia* 5(2): 113–19.

Measham, F. (1996). The 'Big Bang' approach to sessional drinking: changing patterns of alcohol consumption amongst young people in North West England. *Addiction Research* 4(3): 283–99.

Measham, F., Newcombe, R. and Parker, H. (1994). The normalisation of recreational drug use amongst young people in North West England. *British Journal of Sociology* 45: 287–312.

Meltzer, H., Gill, B. and Pettigrew, M. (1995) *The Prevalence of Psychiatric Morbidity among Adults aged 16–64 living in private households in Great Britain.* London: OPCS Publications Unit.

Midanik, L. (1982). The validity of self-reported alcohol consumption and alcohol problems: a literature review. *British Journal of Addiction* 77: 357–82.

Milburn, K., Fraser, E., Secker, J. and Pavis, S. (1995). Combining methods in health promotion research: some considerations about appropriate use. *Health Education Journal* **54**: 347–56.

Miller, P. M. and Plant, M. (1996). Drinking, smoking and illicit drug use among 15 and 16 year olds in the United Kingdom. *British Medical Journal* **313**(7054): 394–7.

Miller, W. R. and Rollnick, S. (1991). *Motivational Interviewing*. London: Guilford.

Moore, L, Smith, C. and Catford, J. (1994). Binge drinking: prevalence patterns and policy. *Health Education Research* **9**(4): 497–505.

MORI (1994). *Attitudes of the General Public towards Policy Issues on Alcohol*. Report for the HEA. Unpublished.

NACRO (1997). *Facts about Young Offenders in 1996*. Youth Crime section Factsheet. London: NACRO.

Nelson, E. and White, D. (1992). Humour and alcohol: children's favourite TV adverts. *Health Education Journal* **51**(2): 64–7.

Newcombe, R., Measham, F. and Parker, H. (1995). A survey of drinking and deviant behaviour among 14–15 year olds in North West England. *Addiction Research* **2**(4): 319–41.

NHS Health Advisory Service (1996). *The Substance of Young Needs: Children and Young People. Substance Misuse Services*. London: HMSO.

Niblett, P. (1995). *Drinking and Driving*. London: Department of Transport.

NOP Market Research Limited (1990). *Beliefs about Alcohol*. London: HEA.

NTC Publications (1994). *The Drinks Pocket Book*. Oxford: NTC Publications.

NTC Publications (1997). *The Drink Pocket Book 1998*. Oxford: NTC Publications.

O'Connor, J. (1978). T*he Young Drinkers*. London: Tavistock.

Office for National Statistics (1997a). *Preliminary Results from the 1996 General Household Survey*. London: HMSO.

Office for National Statistics (1997b). *The Health of Adult Britain 1841–1994, Volume 1: Decennial Supplement Number 12*. London: HMSO.

Office for National Statistics (1997c). *Family Spending. a Report on the 1996 Family Expenditure Survey*. London: HMSO.

Office for National Statistics (1997d). *Health Survey for England, 1996*. London: HMSO.

Office for National Statistics (1998). *Living in Britain: Results from the 1996 General Household Survey*. London: Stationery Office.

Office of Population Censuses and Surveys (1992). *General Household Survey 1990*. London: HMSO.

Oostveen, T., Knibbe, R. and De Vries, H. (1996). Social influences on young adults' alcohol consumption: norms, modelling, pressure, socialising and conformity. *Addictive Behaviours* **21**(2): 187–97.

OPCS (1991). *Drinking in England and Wales in the late 1980s*. London: HMSO.

OPCS (1994). *General Household Survey 1992*. London: HMSO.

OPCS (1995). *Health Survey for England 1993*. London: HMSO.

Orford, J. (1990). Alcohol and the family. In Koslowski, L. T. *et al.* (eds). *Research Advances in Alcohol and Drug Problems*. New York: Plenum, pp.81–155.

Parker, H. (1996). Young adult offenders, alcohol and criminology cul-de-sacs. *British Journal of Criminology* 36(2): 282–98.

Parker, H. (1995). Youth Culture and the Changing Patterns of Drinking by Young People. Paper presented at conference on Alcohol and the Young, 14 December 1995, National Children's Bureau/Royal College of Physicians.

Parker, H. and Measham, F. (1994). Pick 'n' mix. Changing patterns of illicit drug use amongst 1990s adolescents. *Drugs, Education, Prevention and Policy* 1: 5–13.

Pavis, S., Cunningham-Burleys, S. and Amos, A. (1997). Alcohol consumption and young people: exploring meaning and social context. *Health Education Research* 12(3): 311–22.

Pendleton, L., Smith, C. and Roberts, J. L (1988). Monitoring alcohol advertisements on television – developing a consensus approach. *Health Education Journal* 47 (213): 71–3.

Pikkarainen, P. and Raiha, N. C. (1969). Development of alcohol dehydrogenase activity in the human liver. *Nature* 222: 563–4.

Plant, M., Bagnall, G. and Foster, D. (1990). Teenage heavy drinkers: alcohol related knowledge, beliefs, experiences, motivation and the social context of drinking. *Alcohol and Alcoholism* 25(6): 691–8.

Plant, M. A. (1990). Alcohol, sex and AIDS. *Alcohol and Alcoholism* 25: 293–301.

Plant, M. A., Bagnall, G., Foster, J. and Sales, J. (1990). Young people and drinking: results of an English National survey. *Alcohol and Alcoholism* 25: 685–90.

Plant, M. A. and Plant, M. L. (1993). *Risk Takers. Alcohol, Drugs, Sex and Youth*. London: Tavistock/Routledge.

Plant, M., Peck, D. and Samuel, E. (1985). *Alcohol, Drugs and School Leavers*. London: Tavistock.

Portman Group (1993). Britain's young adults – responsible attitudes to drink driving. Press release, 1 December 1993. London: The Portman Group.

Power, C. (1992). Drinking careers: lifestyles and life circumstances. In *Alcohol and Young People: Learning to Cope.* Proceedings of Addictions Forum, Alcohol Research Group Conference, October 1992. London: The Portman Group.

Prescott-Clarke, P. and Primatesta, P. (1997). *Health Survey for England 1995.* London: Stationery Office.

Raskin White, H., Hansell, S. and Brick, J. (1993). Alcohol use and aggression among youth. *Alcohol, Health and Research World* **17** (2): 144–50.

Raw, M. and McNeill, A. (1997). *Young People and Alcohol: a Survey of Attitudes and Behaviour towards New Types of Alcoholic Drinks in England.* London: HEA.

Roberts. C., Blakey, V. and Tudor-Smith, C. (1997). *The Impact of Alcopops on the Drinking Patterns of Young People in Wales.* Findings from the 1996 Welsh Youth Health Survey. Briefing Report Number 12, June 1997. Cardiff: Health Promotion Wales.

Roberts, C., Kingdon, A., Frith, C. and Tudor-Smith, C. (1997). *Young People in Wales: Lifestyle Changes, 1986–1996.* Cardiff: Health Promotion Wales.

Robertson, J. A. and Plant, M. A. (1988). Alcohol, sex and risks of HIV infection. *Drug and Alcohol Dependence* **22**: 75–8.

Robinson, J. (1989). *The Demon Drink.* London: Mitchell Beazley and Mandarin.

Robson, W. J. (1997). Alcohol and young people. *Alcoholism, the Newsletter from the MCA* **16** (6): 1–2.

Rowlands, O. (1998). Experiences of and attitudes towards intoxication among people aged 16 and over in England. London: HEA. Unpublished report.

Royal College of Physicians (1995). *Alcohol and the Young.* Report of joint working party of the Royal College of Physicians and the British Paediatric Association. London: Royal College of Physicians.

Sabey, B. and Coding, P. (1975). Alcohol and road accidents in Great Britain. In Israelstam, S. and Lamber, S. (eds). *Alcohol, Drugs and Road Safety.* Toronto: Addiction Research Foundation.

Saffer, H. (1991). Alcohol advertising bans and alcohol abuse: an international perspective. *Journal of Health Economics* **10** (1): 65–79.

Saffer, H. (1996). Studying the effects of alcohol advertising on consumption. *Alcohol Health and Research World* **20** (4): 266–9.

Scott J. (1992). cited in Donovan, C. and McEwan, R. A review of the literature examining the relationship between alcohol use and HIV-related sexual risk taking in young people. *Addiction* **90**: 319–28.

Shanks (1990). Alcohol and youth. *World Health Forum* **11**: 235–41.

Sharp, D. and Lowe, G. (1989). Adolescents and alcohol – a review of the recent British research. *Journal of Adolescence* **12**: 295–307.

Shepherd, J. and Brinkley, J. (1996). The relationship between alcohol intoxication, stressors and injury in urban violence. *British Journal of Criminology* **36**(4): 546–66.

Sherrat, E., MacArthur, C. and Cheng, K. K. (1997). *West Midlands Young People's Lifestyle Survey 1995–1996: Main Findings.* Birmingham: NHS Executive, West Midlands/University of Birmingham.

Shucksmith, J. (1994). *Children, Families and Alcohol.* Report for HEBS and Barnardo's. Aberdeen: University of Aberdeen.

Slater, M. D., Rouner, D., Murphy, K., Beauvais, F., Vanleuven, J. and Domenech-Rodriguez, M. (1996). Male adolescents' reactions to TV beer advertisements: the effect of sports content and programming context. *Journal of Studies on Alcohol* **57** (4): 425–33.

Slater, M. D., Rouner, D., Murphy, K., Beauvais, F., Van Leuven, J. and Domenech-Rodriguez, M. (1996b). Adolescent counter arguing of TV beer advertisements: evidence for effectiveness of alcohol education and critical viewing discussions. *Journal of Drug Addiction* **26**(2): 141–58.

Smith, C., Roberts, J. L. and Pendleton, L. (1988). Booze on the box. Health Education Research **3**: 267–72.

Smith, M. and Harding, G. (1989). Health Education and Young People. TCRU Occasional Paper No. 9. London: Thomas Coram Research Institute.

Spiegler, D. L. (1983). Children's attitudes towards alcohol. *Journal of Studies on Alcohol* **44**: 545–52.

Squires, T. and Busuttil, A. (1995). Child Fatalities in Scottish house fires 1980–1990: a cause of child neglect. *Child Abuse and Neglect* **19** (7): 865–73.

Staffordshire Police (1997). *Burslem Divisional Consultative Panel 1996/97: Questionnaire Results*. Burslem, Staffs: Staffordshire Police.

Strickland, D. E. (1983). Advertising exposure, alcohol consumption and misuse of alcohol. In Grant, M., Plant, M. and Williams A., (eds). *Economics and Alcohol: Consumption and Controls*. London: Croom Helm, pp. 201–222.

Sumner, M. and Parker, H. (1995). *Low in Alcohol*. London: The Portman Group.

Sutton, S. (1987). Social psychological approaches to understanding addictive behaviours: attitude, behaviour and decision models. *British Journal of Addiction* **82**: 355–70.

Swadi, H. (1989). Truancy and adolescent substance abuse: exploring the links. *European Journal of Psychiatry* 3: 108–15.

TACADE (1987). *Alcohol Education Syllabus*. Salford: TACADE.

TACADE (1994). *Evaluation of the Animation Project*. Salford: TACADE. Unpublished.

Tierney, J., Cohen, J. and Bates, C. (1991). *Two Pints of Lager and a Packet of Crisps Please: a Study of Young People's Use of Pubs in Tameside*. Tameside: Tameside and Glossop Health Authority.

Traeen, B. and Kvalem, I. (1996). Sex under the influence of alcohol among Norwegian adolescents. *Addiction* 91(7): 995–1006.

Tuck, M. (1989). *Drinking and Disorder. Home Office Planning Unit Report No. 108*. London: HMSO.

Turtle, J., Jones, A. and Hickman, M. (1997). *Young People and Health: the Health Behaviour of School Age Children*. London: HEA/BMRB.

Van de Goor, I., Knibbe, R. and Drop, M. (1990). Adolescent drinking behaviour: an observational study of the influence of situational factors on adolescent drinking rate. *Journal of Studies on Alcohol* 51: 548–55.

Velleman, R. (1993). Alcohol and the Family. London: Institute of Alcohol Studies.

Velleman, R. and Orford, J. (1993). The adult adjustment of offspring of parents with drinking problems. *British Journal of Psychiatry* 162: 503–16.

Walker, A. (1997). *Prove it! Proof of Age Card Scheme: Surveys of Cardholders and Off-licence Managers*. London: The Portman Group.

Walker, F. (1997a). 4,000 or 40,000? How many die from alcohol? *Acquire* 16: 6–8.

Walker, F. (1997b). Young people's drinking. *Acquire* 19: 4–6.

Webb, E., Ashton, C. H., Kelly, P. and Kamali, F. (1996). Alcohol and drug use in United Kingdom university students. Lancet **348** (5 October): 922–5.

Werch, C. E., Gorman, D. and Marty, P. (1987). Relationship between alcohol consumption and alcohol problems in young adults. *Journal of Drug Education* **17**: 261-76.

West, M. O. and Prinz, R. J. (1987). Parental alcoholism and childhood psychopathology. *Psychological Bulletin* **102**: 214–18.

West, R., Drummond, C. and Eames, K. (1990). Alcohol consumption, problem drinking and anti-social behaviour in a sample of college students. *British Journal of Addiction* **85**(4): 479–86.

Whitbread Beer Company (1996). *The FAB Report.* London: Whitbread Beer Company.

Wiers, R. W., Hoogeveen, K. J., Sergeant, J. A. and Gunning, W. B. (1997). High and low-dose alcohol-related expectancies and differential associations with drinking in male and female adolescents and young adults. *Addiction* **92**(7): 871–88.

Wilks, J., Callan, V. J. and Austin, D. A. (1989). Parent, peer and personal determinants of adolescent drinking. *British Journal of Addiction* **84**: 619–30.

Wood, D. (1986). *Beliefs about alcohol.* London: HEA.

Wright, L. (1991). *Alcohol and Youth Workers.* Salford: TACADE.

Wright, L. (1993). *More Drinking Choices.* London: HEA.

Wright, L. (1995). *Review of the Drinkwise Campaign 1989–1994.* Report to the Health Education Authority. Unpublished.

Wright, L. and Buczkiwicz, M. (1995). *Awaaz: Asian Young Women and Alcohol.* Salford: TACADE.

Wylie, A. and Casswell, S. (1991). A qualitative investigation of young men's drinking in New Zealand. *Health Education Research* 6(1): 49–55.

Yates, D. W. (1987). The detection of problem drinkers in the accident and emergency department. *British Journal of Addiction* 82: 163–7.

Yates, F. E. (1994). The therapeutic application of a computer problem solving programme to teach coping strategies to problem drinkers. *New Technology in the human services* 7(4): 15–20.

Young, K. (1990). *Danger or Opportunity: Toward a Core Curriculum for the Youth Service.* Leicester: National Youth Agency.